CO

FOSSILS

Text by David M. Martill
Illustrations by Mark Iley

HarperCollins*Publishers*

HarperCollins*Publishers* Ltd
First published 1995

ISBN 0 00 470493 2

Reprint 9 8 7 6 5 4 3 2 1 0

Special thanks to Department of Geology, University
of Leicester

Printed in Italy by Amadeus S.p.A.

CONTENTS AND KEY

How to use this book

This book presents a broad selection of plants and animals, and some of their traces found as fossils in Europe. There is such a vast number of fossil species, that no single book could attempt to provide anything but a small selection from the vast span of geological time represented in the rocks of Europe. Therefore this guide serves to provide general fossil identifications with information on their geological age and distribution.

In addition it also covers aspects of the processes involved in fossilization, how to collect fossils, and some of the uses to which fossils are put.

Major groups of fossils are illustrated and some of the anatomical features that are important in the identification of the various genera are shown. Morphological terms are highlighted in **bold**. Generic names are highlighted in *italics* and are in **bold** when first used. Stratigraphic ranges of particular fossil species are in a different fount. Geographic distributions are given for many fossils, but fossils that are common over most of Europe are listed as cosmopolitan.

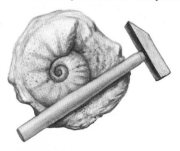

INTRODUCTION

Fossils are common. They can be found wherever there are sedimentary rocks that were formed over the last 550 million years, and have been found and studied ever since man gained an awareness of his environment. To some civilizations fossils were ornamental, being used as tokens or jewellery items. Yet other civilizations, recognizing fossils as the remains of animals and plants, developed stories of dragons turned to stone to explain them. The Greek mythological character of Perseus was able to turn both monsters and men to stone using the ugly, writhing, snake-locked head of the hideous Medusa. The foundations of such tales may well be associated with the discovery of fossil remains, which have always been abundant in the Mediterranean region. The fossils would have been of animals quite unfamiliar and very different to those native to the region 2000-3000 years ago.

In western Europe fossils began to be studied scientifically about 200 years ago, but were still regarded as rather curious objects, and were used by many as evidence of the great biblical flood. Indeed this most famous of biblical stories may well owe its origins to the abundance of fossil remains in the Holy Land. By Victorian times, the study of fossils, or *palaeontology*, had become a respected science, and was taught at both Oxford and Cambridge. The Victorian public were treated to dinosaur hype, just as today. Palaeontology offered the young and old, the rich and poor and the learned and less well-educated an exciting glimpse of life before man.

Today palaeontology is a hobby as well as a vocation, vigorously pursued by many. Collecting fossils has become a major pastime in developed nations, and offers people a dynamic way of looking at the ancient past.

Indeed, it is the amateur palaeontologist who often makes the most exciting finds. Dinosaurs turn up in the most unlikely places. The new European dinosaur *Baryonyx* was found in a brick pit just south of London, not by a professional, but by an amateur collector. The oldest fossil ever found in England was discovered by a schoolboy, Roger Mason, in a park in Leicestershire. Such exciting discoveries are made almost every year. Persistence and diligent searching will bring rewards to all who collect fossils. The more one searches for fossils, the more practised the eye becomes.

Joining a local geological society will aid collecting, as most societies have regular field trips, often to places that may be inaccessible to individuals, especially mine and quarry visits. Local museums may offer identification services, often at no charge, and may also be able to give advice on where to collect fossils locally.

What are fossils?

Fossils are the remains or traces of ancient life left behind as a record in the rocks. Three broad groups of fossils are currently recognized:

1) Body fossils

These are the most commonly collected fossils and are discussed further below (see p. 13).

2) Trace fossils

These fossils are the record of tracks, trails and burrows left by organisms in sediment (see p. 12).

3) Molecular fossils

Molecular fossils are not treated here as they require sophisticated analytical tools to be studied. They are the molecules or decomposition products of biomolecules that occur only in living organisms that have been incorporated into sediments. Oil could be thought of as a mixture of molecular fossils.

The ancient Greeks used the term fossil to refer to anything dug from the ground, but today such remains as Roman coins and pottery are called artefacts and are not regarded as fossils. They are studied by archaeologists, whereas fossils are studied by palaeontologists and geologists. There is only a vague line between palaeontology and archaeology. Those people who study the very early history of man have a foot in both camps and are called palaeoanthropologists.

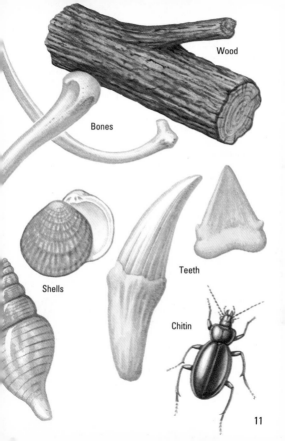

Wood

Bones

Shells

Teeth

Chitin

11

Trace fossils

Trace fossils are the tracks, trails, footprints, burrows and borings left by organisms in sediment that are preserved when the sediment becomes rock. They are very common in some marine sediments, and may have complex structures. The most common trace fossils are made by marine annelids, arthropods and molluscs that burrow in the sediment, either to hide or to find food. Sometimes the activity of these animals is so intense that it completely churns the sediment destroying any of the original fabric. This process is called **bioturbation**, and the degree of bioturbation can be used as a rough indicator of the oxygen concentration on the sea floor. Only occasionally is the animal that made the track or burrow present.

Dinosaur track way

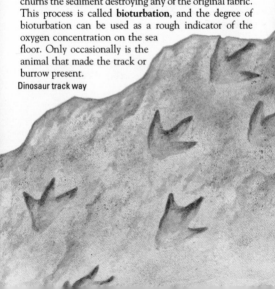

Body fossils

Body fossils are the tangible remains of organisms, and include a wide variety of elements such as teeth, bones, shells and arthropod **exoskeletons**. Plants also produce body fossils such as leaves, wood, fruits and flowers. Body fossils are usually the most obvious fossils found in rocks, and are the most frequently studied. They may be found preserved in a wide variety of styles (see p. 21) in most types of sedimentary rocks of all ages except the **Archaean**. The actual remains of the organism need not be present, as even an impression is considered to be a body fossil.

Trilobite exoskeleton, a typical body fossil

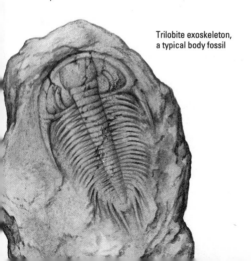

Micro fossils

Micro fossils are simply small body fossils that must be examined with a hand lens, an optical microscope, or in some cases, can only be seen with an electron microscope. Micro fossils are often exceptionally beautiful, and frequently very well preserved. They can be so abundant that a kilogramme of rock will contain literally millions of micro fossils. They can easily be collected by gently washing clays through a nest of fine sieves down to 100 micron mesh size. Micro fossils include pollen and spores from plants, very small teeth from larval fish, tooth-like conodonts and small crustaceans such as ostracods. A number of single-celled organisms produce microscopic **tests** which can also become fossils, including **silica** tests of radiolaria and **calcitic** foraminiferans.

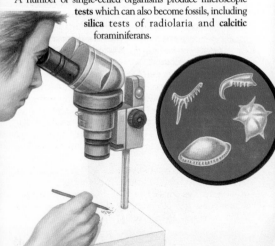

Uses of fossils

Fossils have a number of important commercial uses, the most important being as **biostratigraphic indicators** (see p. 18), which means that they can be used to date rocks. This enables geologists to guess how old one set of rocks is relative to another. This is particularly important in drilling for mineral and hydrocarbon resources such as coal, gas, oil and metal ores. Geologists collect the chippings produced by the drill bit to discover what type of rock they are drilling through, then collect the micro fossils from within the chippings to determine the rocks relative age, as each geological time period is characterized by different fossil forms. A more recent application has been to determine the rate at which climate has changed over time, and to monitor types of climate using fossil plants and insects. Fossil plants are particularly useful, as leaf shape and cuticle thickness are important in determining relative humidity, rainfall and temperature.

Another scientific use of fossils is mapping their distribution to plot the way continental plates have moved and split apart. This technique relies heavily on terrestrial organisms, or the fossils of animals that live only in shallow sea water, and are unable to migrate large distances. Fossils from rocks in Brazil and in southwest Africa proved that these two continents were joined together about 250 million years ago.

In historic times fossil sea urchins were used as weights on market stalls, while trilobites have been used as a form of currency. Today fossil tree resin, or amber, is prized as a semi-precious gem stone and fossils are widely traded as novel ornaments and souvenirs.

Fossils are used to correlate rocks of similar age between distant localities. In the diagram below a sequence of fossiliferous rocks in three different areas show the same sequence of fossils through time, although some fossil groups are absent in some areas. Silurian rocks are present in areas A and C. Above this a sequence of unfossiliferous rocks is presumed to be of Devonian age in A and C because it is overlain in all areas by Carboniferous rocks. It cannot be presumed to be Devonian in area B as it is not underlain by rocks containing older fossils. Permo/Triassic rocks are only present in B and C, Jurassic and Cretaceous rocks are present in all areas.

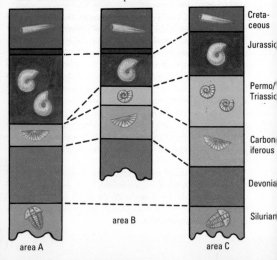

Creta-
ceous

Jurassic

Permo/
Triassic

Carbon
iferous

Devonia

Silurian

area A

area B

area C

Evolution and extinction

Fossils offer a unique opportunity to examine ancient organisms and the way and rate at which life on Earth has evolved. It was fossil remains that finally convinced Charles Darwin that some form of transition from one species to another must have occurred. Not only do fossils show that evolution has taken place, they also provide important clues and insights into when and how life evolved on Earth.

Remarkably, the fossil record shows that life appeared very early in Earth's history, probably over four billion years ago. The fossil record is very poor in the Precambrian, but it shows a gradual increase in complexity of organisms, and late Precambrian rocks show that a variety of multicellular organisms were present. It was only with the biological invention of the skeleton that fossils become common. An evolutionary explosion occurred about 560 million years ago. At this time most of the **phyla** (groups) alive today appeared for the first time. This time is taken to mark the beginning of the **Phanerozoic Era**.

In addition to the appearance of new forms of organisms, the fossil record also shows that species become extinct. In several periods the rate of extinction of animals and plants increased to such an extent that mass extinctions occurred. Some extinctions were caused by terrestrial phenomena, probably related to climatic changes due to the movement of continents, while others, notably the mass extinction at the end of the Cretaceous when the dinosaurs became extinct, may have been caused by extra-terrestrial events, such as large meteorite impacts.

Different rates of evolution are revealed by the fossil record. The brachiopod *Lingula* today looks almost exactly like *Lingula* found in Ordovician rocks, while the ammonites evolved into many very distinct forms over relatively short geological time spans and are now extinct.

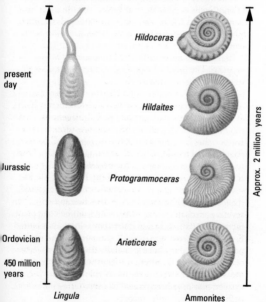

present day

Jurassic

Ordovician

450 million years

Hildoceras

Hildaites

Protogrammoceras

Arieticeras

Approx. 2 million years

Lingula

Ammonites

How fossils are formed

Many processes act upon the remains of dead organisms that result in their preservation as fossils. Unfortunately there are many more processes that act upon organic remains to deprive us of fossils. Only a small percentage of the animals and plants that have lived on Earth ever become fossils. Despite this, fossils are extremely common and can be a major component of sedimentary rocks. Some animals have skeletons composed of minerals that do not undergo any, or only very little, change when they are buried. The calcite shells of some bivalves for example. But many shells do undergo change.

The most common way in which a shell becomes a fossil is that after burial the shell is filled with sediment which then turns to rock by a process called **diagenesis**. The sediment on the outside of the shell also turns to rock. The rock that fills the inside of the shell is a fossil, known as the **internal mould**. The rock around the outside of the shell is also a fossil, known as the **external mould**. Sometimes the shell may be dissolved away by slightly acidic waters. The resulting cavity is called a **composite mould**. Should the cavity become filled with a new mineral, the fossil that results is called a **cast**. Casts can be composed of many different minerals. If the new mineral has faithfully replicated the structure of the shell it is called a **replacement**. Some shells, especially those that are composed originally of the mineral aragonite, undergo a transformation and convert into the mineral calcite. This is called **neomorphism** and is very common in ammonites.

Death of a large terrestrial animal

Scavenging of carcass may disrupt the skeleton (below)

Decay by bacteria removes most organic material, skeleton then buried in mud by a flooding river (below)

There are some rather unusual ways in which organic remains can be fossilized. One of the most spectacular types of fossilization is preservation in amber, the fossil resin of ancient trees. Resin oozing from ancient trees trapped insects (see illustration on p. 27) and even small lizards. Natural antibiotics in the resin prevented the trapped animals from decomposing, and the dry nature of the resin caused dehydration and ultimately perfectly preserved the inclusion. Genetic information has even been taken from such fossils in the form of short strands of DNA.

The frozen wastes of Alaska and Siberia have yielded remarkable animals trapped in frozen ground. These include the remains of woolly mammoth, woolly rhinoceros and giant ox. These fossils have some soft tissues preserved, reportedly in an edible condition. This kind of preservation is unusual, and restricted to animals only a few thousand years old.

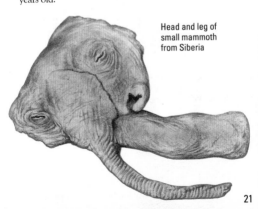

Head and leg of
small mammoth
from Siberia

Many fossils are found crushed flat on **bedding planes**. This flattening is due to the weight of the overlying sediment. Such flattening is very common in clays and shales, which are easily compacted. Fossils in shales that have not been flattened are usually filled with a mineral which has been able to withstand the weight of the overlying rock.

There are other cases where fossils are particularly well preserved, and include evidence not just of the skeleton, but also of soft tissues and even stomach contents. The key to excellent preservation appears to be rapid burial in sediment, and rapid diagenesis. The process of fossilization has to be faster than the processes of scavenging and bacterial decomposition.

Shell in life position within sediment

After death new minerals form in shell

Later compression may flatten fossil due to weight of overlying sediment

Mineralization

Mineralization, the formation of minerals in rocks, is important for the formation of rock itself and of fossils. The growth of minerals in sediment is the process that changes sand into sandstone, or shell accumulations into limestone and is called **diagenesis**. The growth of minerals in holes formed where shells have dissolved out produces fossil casts.

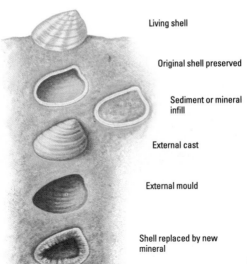

Living shell

Original shell preserved

Sediment or mineral infill

External cast

External mould

Shell replaced by new mineral

Cracks produced in rocks that are buried deeply, or are in areas of active earthquakes may be cemented together by the growth of minerals in those cracks. These aspects of mineralization serve to preserve fossils. Sometimes mineralization can be detrimental, and may destroy fossils, by replacing all the original fabric of the rock, including its fossils, with new minerals. Areas of intense mineralization generally do not produce good fossils, but areas of light mineralization can produce exceptional fossils.

Sedimentary rocks

Fossils mostly occur in sedimentary rocks which are produced by the cementing together of sediment particles. The sediment is produced in a number of ways:

- sand, silt and clay particles are produced by the weathering and erosion of pre-existing rocks by the elements of wind, rain, flowing water and frost
- limestones are made from broken bits of shell material
- peat, lignite or coal (each is differentiated by how hard it is) are made from organic plant debris
- evaporites are made by chemical precipitation, usually due to evaporation, in hot arid regions. Fossils are not usually common in them.

Fossils are most abundant in clays and shales, and in limestones. In general, coarse grained rocks such as gritstones and pebble beds often have broken and worn fossils, whereas fine grained rocks tend to have well preserved fossils.

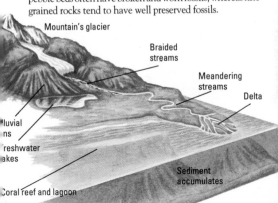

Mountain's glacier

Braided streams

Meandering streams

Delta

Alluvial fans

Freshwater lakes

Sediment accumulates

Coral reef and lagoon

Common sedimentary minerals

Sedimentary rocks often contain distinctive minerals. The most common of these are quartz, calcite, dolomite, pyrite, siderite and goethite. These minerals may be found replacing fossils.

- Calcite is common and is found as veins or filling cavities in rocks. Fossils that have hollow centres are often lined with crystals of this mineral. Calcite will fizz in dilute hydrochloric acid.
- Quartz is hard and will scratch glass. Calcite and quartz are usually white or clear.
- Dolomite is similar to calcite, but often has a buff colour.
- Siderite may be white or brown.
- Pyrite is very distinctive, with a shiny brass colour. It is sometimes called fool's gold and is very heavy.
- Goethite may be black, brown or yellow. It sometimes looks like rust. Fossils that are composed of pyrite may convert to goethite after being exposed for a long period.

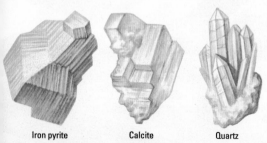

Iron pyrite   Calcite   Quartz

Exceptional fossils

A few localities in Europe have become famous for a very high quality of fossil preservation. At these sites the fossils often have very fine detail, even of soft tissues. Some of the most notable sites are in Germany.

At Solnhofen in Bavaria, fine grained, laminated limestones have yielded fossils of the oldest bird, complete with feathers (see p. 199), while in Holzmaden, also in southern Germany, Jurassic shales yield complete skeletons of fishes, crocodiles and ichthyosaurs, some with the outline of the skin (see p. 187) and stomach contents. Such sites have become Meccas for palaeontologists.

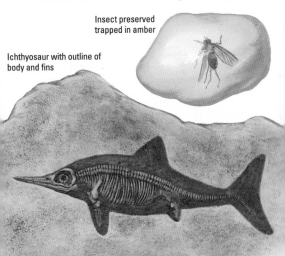

Insect preserved
trapped in amber

Ichthyosaur with outline of
body and fins

Collecting fossils

Collecting fossils is a great open-air pastime. It takes you to some of the most beautiful landscapes and coastlines, offers the thrill that you may discover something very exciting, such as a dinosaur, and is harmless to the environment.

Fossils can be collected in many places, and only a small selection of areas are indicated on the maps on p. 32 and p. 34-5. For Europe we have only listed a few of the more spectacular sites, most of which have a local museum with displays of the wonderful fossils to be found. Local museums can often provide good advice on where to collect fossils and where to obtain permission to look for them.

Equipment needed for fossil collecting varies depending on what you are looking for. As a rule the field collector should carry a geological hammer, a couple of cold chisels, a hand lens, a penknife, some wrapping paper and tins for small specimens. A geological map may be useful, but a note book and pencil to record locality details will mean that you can look up the geological map at a later date. A strong rucksack is essential, as a day's collection can be very heavy. Do not try to do any fine preparation in the field; take the fossil home in a lump of rock, and extract it later with fine tools. Try not to over collect. Over collecting has become a problem at some European localities. If you have to extract your discovery from a large piece of rock, always work away from the fossil. A chisel that slips can easily damage the exposed parts of the fossil. If you find a large skeleton, do not attempt to collect it, but seek the help of an expert.

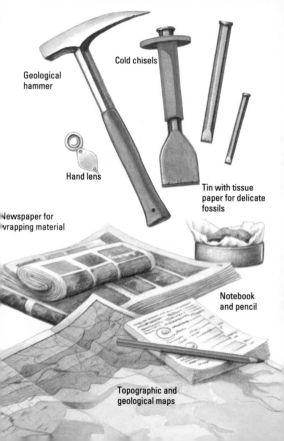

Geological hammer

Cold chisels

Hand lens

Tin with tissue paper for delicate fossils

Newspaper for wrapping material

Notebook and pencil

Topographic and geological maps

Safety

Collecting fossils has its hazards and there are a number of points to bear in mind.

- If going into wild country, tell someone where you are going, and never go alone. Take food and drink.
- If you are working on the coast check the tides and always keep an eye on the rising tide.
- Never work under cliffs, they often fall down.
- Be very careful when climbing over clay landslips, seemingly firm ground can suddenly liquefy.
- Always seek permission to go into quarries and mines. Quarry faces are very unstable, and quarry dump trucks can suddenly come round a blind corner with 100 tonnes of rock on board. Listen out for blast sirens.
- When near old mines, watch out for any uncovered mine shafts.
- Never enter caves without proper caving equipment.
- Wear safety goggles when using a hammer and chisel, and never, never hit a hammer with another hammer.
- Wear a hard hat when in a working quarry or near cliffs.

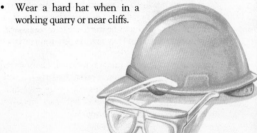

Where to find fossils

Almost anywhere where there are sedimentary rocks you may find fossils, but fossils are more common in some places than others.

Precambrian rocks only very rarely contain body fossils and any found should not be collected; these are rocks for experts. From the Cambrian onward, it is quite easy to find excellent fossils. As there are hardly any areas of Precambrian rocks in Europe, except for Scotland and Scandinavia, almost anywhere is a good place to go. You should check a geological map to see what ages the rocks are where you plan to visit, as this will help determine the types of fossil you can expect to find.

- Clays, shales, limestones and marine sandstones are usually the best.
- Fossils are often found where rocks are being exposed by active erosion, such as sea cliffs and river banks, and in working quarries: in the face or on spoil dumps.
- Areas where clay cliffs are being eroded by the sea continuously yield new fossils; they are best visited after the winter storms have washed out new fossils.
- Beaches in front of cliffs can be good places to pick up loose fossils but they may be worn due to wave activity. Sandstones formed in non-marine environments are often very poor in fossils.
- Rocks that have been metamorphosed, i.e. changed by heat and pressure, have often had their fossils destroyed although in the Swiss Alps many metamorphic rocks still contain fossils, but they are often misshapen and highly recrystallized.

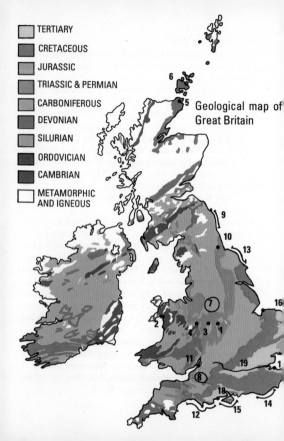

TERTIARY

CRETACEOUS

JURASSIC

TRIASSIC & PERMIAN

CARBONIFEROUS

DEVONIAN

SILURIAN

ORDOVICIAN

CAMBRIAN

METAMORPHIC
AND IGNEOUS

Geological map of
Great Britain

Fossil localities in Great Britain

These locations all currently yield well preserved and abundant fossils.

Cambrian
1) Nuneaton

Ordovician
2) North Wales

Silurian
3) Wren's Nest, Dudley
4) Wenlock Edge

Devonian
5) Caithness
6) Orkney Isles

Lower Carboniferous
7) Derbyshire, White Peak
8) Mendips

Upper Carboniferous
9) Northumberland coast

Permian
10) Writhlington, County Durham

Triassic
11) Aust Cliff, Avon

Jurassic
12) Dorset coast
13) Yorkshire coast

Cretaceous
14) Sussex coast
15) Isle of Wight, South coast
16) Norfolk coast

Tertiary
17) Isle of Sheppey, Kent
18) Barton on Sea, Hampshire

Pleistocene
19) Gravel Pits in Thames Valley
20) Walton on the Naze, Essex

Geological map of Europe

Important palaeontological sites:
1. Halstatt, Austria. Triassic
2. Cerin, France. Jurassic
3. Boulogne, France. Jurassic/ Cretaceous
4. Dives, France. Jurassic
5. Holzmaden, Germany. Jurassic
6. Messel, Germany. Eocene
7. Solnhofen, Germany. Jurassic
8. Monte Bolca, Italy. Eocene
9. Monte San Giorgio, Switzerland/ Italy. Triassic
10. Montsech, Spain. Cretaceous
11. Gotland, Sweden. Silurian

QUATERNARY

TERTIARY

CRETACEOUS

JURASSIC

TRIASSIC/PERMIAN

CARBONIFEROUS COAL MEASURES

CAMBRIAN TO LOWER CARBONIFEROUS

CRYSTALLINE BASEMENT

Geological time and dating rocks

The Earth has existed for approximately 5000 million years. Geologists divide this incredibly long time span into segments, the boundaries of which are based on certain events or episodes that make the rocks formed during these periods distinct. There are hierarchies of division, with four super divisions recognizable, the Hadean, the Archaean, the Proterozoic and the Phanerozoic (see chart p. 254-5).

The **Hadean** is the earliest part of Earth's history from the time at which the planet formed until the formation of the first crustal rocks on its surface. For much of this time the Earth had a molten surface, was continuously bombarded by meteorites and probably had no atmosphere.

The **Archaean** is characterized by having no fossils, although recent discoveries have shown that life was present on Earth during some of the Archaean.

The **Proterozoic** is characterized by evidence of simple life, mainly micro fossils of bacteria-like organisms, although later in the Proterozoic more complex life forms evolved.

The **Phanerozoic** is characterized by an abundance of fossils of great diversity. It is from Phanerozoic rocks that most people collect fossils.

The Phanerozoic is divided into three **Eras**: the oldest, the **Palaeozoic** or ancient life era, is characterized by fossil remains of animals and plants that are very different from forms alive today, and the end of the Palaeozoic is marked by a **mass extinction** event.

36

The next era, the **Mesozoic**, or middle life period is one of the best known as this is when the dinosaurs were alive. Many fossils from the Mesozoic are similar to forms alive today, although rarely are the same genera found.

Many fossils from the most recent era, the **Cenozoic** are quite familiar, especially many of the molluscs. The name means recent life. The eras are further subdivided into periods on the basis of their contained fossil remains. The chart on p. 254-5 lists the divisions and gives their ages.

Fossils can only be used to give relative ages to rocks, i.e. which rock is oldest compared to another rock. Absolute ages are obtained by measuring the relative quantities of radioactive elements and their decay products. For example, radioactive potassium forty decays to argon forty. It does so at a constant rate, and it begins only when the mineral that contains the radioactive potassium is formed. Thus volcanic rocks which are rich in minerals containing potassium can be used to obtain real ages, called **radiometric ages**. If the dated volcanic rocks occur within a sequence of sedimentary rocks, it is possible to confine the age of the sedimentary rocks and their fossils. Once the age of a characteristic fossil is found, that fossil can be used to infer the age of the rocks anywhere where that fossil occurs. Fossils that have short time ranges are very useful for this, especially if they have a wide geographic distribution.

FOSSIL INVERTEBRATES

In this book invertebrates include single celled foraminiferans, multicellular sponges, brachiopods and bryozoans, molluscs, annelids, arthropods and echinoderms. Also included are the graptolites which are probably more closely related to vertebrates than they are to any of the invertebrate groups here.

Invertebrates may have internal skeletons (as in sea urchins and starfishes), external skeletons (as in arthropods and many molluscs), or as with many groups, no skeleton with hard parts at all (such as nematodes and many annelids). Thus many invertebrate phyla, nematodes for example, have a poor fossil record.

Skeletons may be single component or multi-component, with some echinoderms having skeletons made of many thousands of elements. Of the invertebrates that do have skeletons, they are composed of a variety of different minerals including calcite, aragonite, calcium phosphates, silica and chitin. Skeletons composed of calcite and calcium phosphate tend to be particularly common in the fossil record. Chitin is less common as it is organic and prone to bacterial decay.

The invertebrate fossil record is very long, going back to the Proterozoic. Invertebrates are also very common, and their remains can frequently be sufficiently abundant to be a major component of limestones, and especially in rocks that are formed in warm, shallow coastal regions, such as coral reefs.

FORAMINIFERA

Foraminifera are single-celled animals that produce delicate chambered tests of calcite, perforated by numerous holes from which extend **pseudopodia** (literally *false feet*) which trap food particles. Foraminifera are usually micro fossils, commonly being less than 1 mm in diameter. They can sometimes be seen on dark coloured clays as small white dots. A few species grew large, multi-chambered shells, up to 30 mm diameter. They can be an important component of limestone; some of the Egyptian pyramids were built of foraminiferan limestone. Two common large foraminiferans are **Nummilites** from the Eocene, which is common over most of Europe, and **Fusilinus** from the Permian of southern Europe, including the Alps of Austria and Italy.

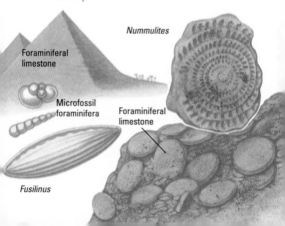

Foraminiferal limestone

Nummulites

Microfossil foraminifera

Foraminiferal limestone

Fusilinus

SPONGES

Sponges are very simple animals consisting usually of a cup-shaped body with a wall perforated by numerous holes. The large opening of the cup is an outlet hole or **osculum**, whereas the small, multiple openings or **ostia** on the wall of the cup are inlets for water currents.

Sponges have no mouth and no organs. They have slight differentiation of cells, with some cells responsible for building a skeleton, and some for generating water currents, but they do not show true tissues. The cells of sponges are capable of reforming if they are split apart.

The main body of the sponge is supported by an internal skeleton which in many forms is composed of an organic substance called **spongin**, which is only very rarely preserved as a fossil. Bath sponges have this type of skeleton. Many sponges have a mineralized skeleton composed either of isolated **spicules** or of a meshwork. Spicules are often composed of silica, whereas many of the robust meshwork type skeletons are composed of calcite. Sponges can be very common as fossils and are known in rocks from the Cambrian to the present day.

Today sponges live in freshwater, shallow seas and in very deep parts of the ocean. They appear to have changed very little over 500 million years.

Stromatoporoids are an extinct group of colonial organisms which constructed a dome-like mass of calcite with fine layering internally. A few forms are cylindrical and branched. The surface is covered with fine holes or stellate furrows called **asterorhizae**. They can be several

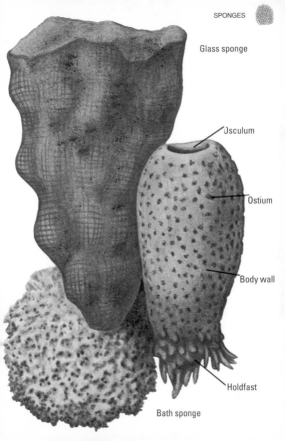

SPONGES

Glass sponge

Osculum

Ostium

Body wall

Holdfast

Bath sponge

Stromatoporoids are an extinct group of colonial organisms which constructed a dome-like mass of calcite with fine layering internally. A few forms are cylindrical and branched. The surface is covered with fine holes or stellate furrows called **asterorhizae**. They can be several hundred millimetres in diameter and are common in reef limestones. Cosmopolitan. **Cambrian** to **Oligocene.**

Siphonia is a common sponge in the chalk of northern Europe, frequently occurring as a silica replacement in flint nodules. It can easily be collected in quantity from beaches in front of chalk cliffs in southern England and northern France. **Middle Cretaceous** to **Tertiary.**

Rhaphidonema is a sponge with a calcareous cup or funnel-like skeleton with numerous small, complex shaped holes on the outer surface of the cup. The base is often expanded to give an hour glass-like appearance. Cosmopolitan. **Triassic** to **Cretaceous.**

Porosphaera is a small calcareous sponge with almost spherical outline generally less than 1 cm diameter. An osculum is visible as a small, rounded opening. Common in the chalk of northwest Europe. **Cretaceous.**

Spicules are usually microscopic, fine needle-like skeletal elements found in some sponges. They may be simple, or complex with radial needles and delicate open cubes. Some deep water sponges have needle-like spicules of great length woven in to delicate basket shapes. They are best seen with a hand lens. **Cambrian** to **present day.**

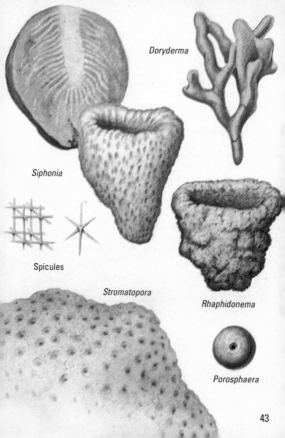

Doryderma

Siphonia

Spicules

Stromatopora

Rhaphidonema

Porosphaera

43

CORALS

Corals are simple organisms belonging to the phylum cnidaria. They may be solitary or colonial and reproduce both sexually and asexually, the latter by simple budding. Many forms produce a calcareous skeleton on which the coral **polyp** sits, called the **theca** or **corallite**. The corallite may possess a series of radial ridges known as **septa**, and in some forms horizontal platforms or **tabulae**. Between the septa, cross walls may be present termed **dissepiments**. In colonial corals individual corallites may be closely packed, open or in some forms separated from each other by cellular material called **coenenchyme**. All corals are marine and most inhabit warm shallow water regions. Living corals are particularly beautiful and the soft parts of the organism are often brightly coloured. Some forms inhabit deeper waters and a few are tolerant of cold water. Almost all fossil corals are also marine forms. Three major groups are recognized as fossils. **Tabulate corals** in which tabulae are developed, **rugose corals** which have prominent major and minor septa, and **scleractinian corals** which include all post Triassic corals.

Colonial corals

Living coral polyp

Solitary corals

Halysites has elongate, round to oval corallites arranged in a chain. Each corallite has a thick wall and complete tabulae. Common in Silurian of England and Sweden. Ordovician to Silurian.

Favosites is a colonial coral forming irregular sub-hemispherical masses with small polygonal corallites. Tabulae complete. Common over most of Europe. Upper Ordovician to Middle Devonian.

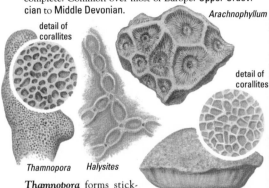

detail of corallites

Arachnophyllum

detail of corallites

Thamnopora   *Halysites*

Favosites

Thamnopora forms stick-like colonies with irregular closely spaced corallites. Common in Devonian of Germany. Closely related forms are widespread in Europe and range from the Silurian to Permian.

Arachnophyllum is colonial with large polygonal corallites. Each corallite is divided into two zones by a circular band of thickened septa. Common in England, Estonia and Sweden. Silurian.

45

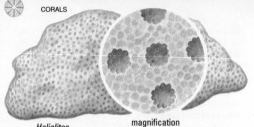

Heliolites   magnification
showing corallites

Heliolites is a low-domed coral forming massive colonies.
The small septate corallites are embedded in a network of
coenenchyme and have 12 small septa. Tabulae are usually complete and horizontal. Cosmopolitan. **Ordovician**
to **Devonian**.

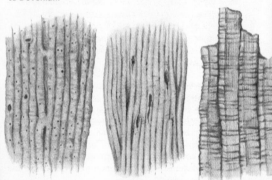

Syringopora   *Siphonodendron
junceum*   *Lithostrotion
portlocki*

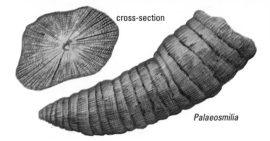

cross-section

Palaeosmilia

Palaeosmilia is a large, conical, often slightly curved solitary coral with prominent growth rings on the outer wall. Fine, longitudinal striations give the outer wall a net-like appearance. The septa are very fine and numerous. Cosmopolitan. **?Upper Devonian** to **Carboniferous.**
Syringopora is a colonial coral composed of numerous tube-like corallites with moderately thick walls connected by thin cross-bars or tubules. There is no coenenchyme between the corallites. Tabulae within the corallites are irregular. Cosmopolitan. **Ordovician** to **Permian.**
Lithostrotions are a group of colonial corals, often reaching considerable size. Corallites may be closely united as in *Lithostrotion portlocki* giving polygonal shaped corallites, or less compact and with circular corallites as in *Siphonodendron junceum*. Cosmopolitan. **Carboniferous** to **Permian.**

47

Dibunophyllum is a solitary cone-shaped coral. Growth lines are prominent on the outer wall and septa extend toward the centre. A central columella is prominent. Cosmopolitan. **Carboniferous.**

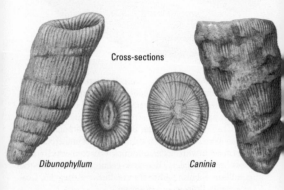

Cross-sections

Dibunophyllum   *Caninia*

Caninia is also a solitary coral with a curved horn-like shape. It may reach a length of 30 cm or more. Septa are prominent but do not reach the centre of the cup. Common in Belgium and the UK. **Carboniferous.**

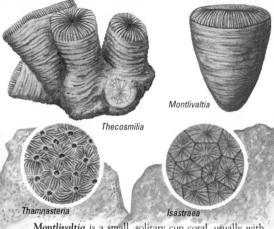

Thecosmilia

Montlivaltia

Thamnasteria

Isastraea

Montlivaltia is a small, solitary cup coral, usually with smooth outer wall, perhaps with faint growth lines. Septa are prominent and project above cup and there is a weak columella. Cosmopolitan. Triassic to Cretaceous.

Thecosmilia is a branched colonial coral. Septa prominent and project above cup. Colonies may reach 1 m in diameter. Cosmopolitan. Triassic to Cretaceous.

Isastraea is a flat or low-domed colonial coral with numerous closely spaced corallites with a well-defined wall between each. Septa may be confluent with those in adjacent corallites. Cosmopolitan. Jurassic to Cretaceous.

Thamnasteria is similar to *Isastraea* but with less well defined boundaries between corallites. Cosmopolitan. Middle Triassic to Cretaceous.

There are many types of coral alive today, many of which are important builders of coral reefs along with bryozoans, algae and a variety of other organisms. The two corals illustrated here are typical modern reef building corals.

Acropora is a branching colonial scleractinian coral. There are over 200 recognizable living species, and many fossil species. It is common and widespread as a fossil over southern Europe. Ranges from the **Eocene** to the **present day**.

Meandrina is a colonial coral with elongate meandering corallites. The corallites are valley-like with numerous septa. Many fossil and living forms recognizable. Common in southern Europe. It ranges from the **Oligocene** to the **present day**.

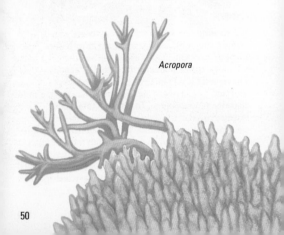

Acropora

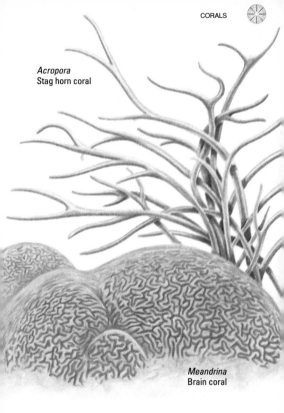

Acropora
Stag horn coral

Meandrina
Brain coral

BRYOZOANS

Bryozoans are small colonial organisms that superficially resemble a coral polyp. The animal, called a **zooid**, lives in a chamber, the **zooecium**, with a small lid or **diaphragm**. The zooecia form part of a larger structure known as the **zoarium**. There may be a special brood chamber known as the **gynozooid** which is larger than the zooecia.

The overall colony may be irregular, and encrusting, stick-like, branching, spherical, fan-like or even screw-shaped. Colonies may grow to several centimetres in diameter, but individual zoecia are always small and generally less than 1 mm diameter. The colony skeleton is usually composed of calcite, but some forms have skeletons of organic material. These non-mineralized forms are rare in the fossil record. All of the forms with calcite skeletons are marine. Bryozoans are very common today, and can easily be found as the lacy network seen encrusting strap-like pieces of seaweed.

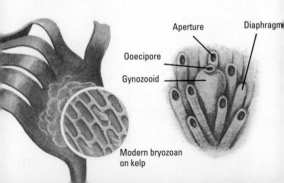

Aperture

Diaphragm

Ooecipore

Gynozooid

Modern bryozoan on kelp

Favositella is a low, encrusting, sheet-like bryozoan colony usually only a few millimetres high. There is some debate as to the true affinities of this fossil, with some believing it might be a type of coral. Common in UK. Ordovician to Silurian.

Fenestella is a common fan or funnel-like bryozoan colony with small cross-struts or dissepiments supporting the branching colony. Each branch has zooecia arranged in pairs on one side only. Cosmopolitan. Ordovician to Permian.

Acanthocladia is a branching colony in which there are robust main branches which repeatedly split into two. From these, numerous finer lateral branches project. The whole forms an erect, bushy colony, usually without dissepiments. Zooecia are only present on one surface. Common in northeast England and Germany. Upper Carboniferous to Permian.

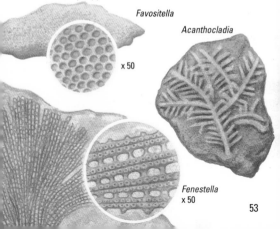

Favositella

x 50

Acanthocladia

Fenestella
x 50

Hyperosopora is a common Jurassic encrusting bryozoan
often found on the surface of large oyster shells. It forms
flat, round to fan-like colonies in which the zooecia are
tube-like. UK and France. **Jurassic**.

Ropalonaria is a common boring bryozoan which produces
a fern-like pattern of borings just below the surface of large
oyster shells. Common in UK. **Ordovician** to **Jurassic**.

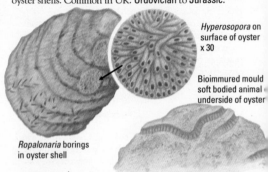

Hyperosopora on
surface of oyster
x 30

Bioimmured mould
soft bodied animal
underside of oyster

Ropalonaria borings
in oyster shell

Bioimmuration

Many oysters cement themselves to stones or rocks. As
they grow over the surface they smother other organisms
living on the same piece of rock and can produce an
external mould of the overgrown animal. This is known
as **bioimmuration** and is important as it provides a means
of finding fossils of encrusting animals that lack hard
skeletons. The most common fossils found in this way are
tiny organic-walled bryozoans.

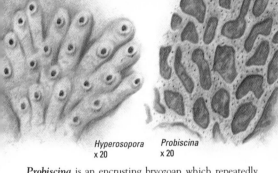

Hyperosopora
x 20

Probiscina
x 20

Probiscina is an encrusting bryozoan which repeatedly branches over the encrusted surface. Each branch has numerous zooecia which have slightly raised walls. Common in Cretaceous chalks on the surface of sea urchins. Cosmopolitan, currently found in the Red Sea. **Jurassic** to **present day**.

Meandropora is a massive, colonial bryozoan, in which the colony is sub-spherical with irregularly **anastomosing** or meandering ridges on the surface. Colonies may reach several centimetres in diameter. Common in southeast England. **Pliocene**.

Meandropora

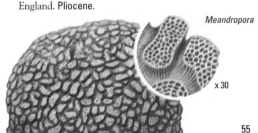

x 30

BRACHIOPODS

Brachiopods resemble bivalved molluscs at first glance, but
in fact they are more closely related to bryozoans than they
are to molluscs. Brachiopods are characterized by possessing
two valves, one of which bears an opening at the posterior
end called the **pedicle foramen**. In life a pedicle passes
through this hole and attaches the brachiopod to the substrate. This valve is called the **pedicle valve**. The other
valve, the **brachial valve**, has on its inside surface a structure,
the **brachidium**, which supports a **lophophore**, an apparatus
for feeding. The shell may be strongly ribbed, and divided
by a deep sulcus, or it may be smooth. Brachiopods are
known from the Cambrian to the present day, and one
genus, *Lingula*, has remained almost unchanged in external
appearance for almost 500 million years.

Brachiopod symmetry

An easy way to distinguish brachiopods from bivalves is
to examine the symmetry of the shells. Brachiopods and
most bivalves are bilaterally symmetrical. In brachiopods
the plane of symmetry cuts each valve in half. There is no

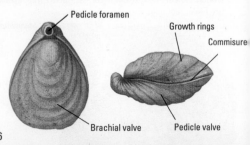

Pedicle foramen

Growth rings

Commisure

Brachial valve

Pedicle valve

Bivalve   Brachiopod

left and right valve. In bivalve molluscs the plane of symmetry divides the valves into mirror image left and right valves.

Inarticulate brachiopods

Lingula belongs to a group of brachiopods known as the inarticulates because there is no hinge, only muscles and a ligament holding the valves together. The shell is phosphatic, and both valves are almost equal in size and shape. Cosmopolitan. *Lingula* is a living fossil and is known from the Ordovician to the present day.

Discinisca is an inarticulate brachiopod which adhered to the surface of other shells such as ammonites. It has an almost circular outline. The cone-shaped brachial valve usually shows concentric growth rings and the pedicle valve has a slit posteriorly. It is cosmopolitan in the Jurassic, but like *Lingula* is alive in the present day.

Lingula   *Discinisca*

57

Articulate brachiopods

Articulate brachiopods form by far the largest group of brachiopods, both alive today and in the past. They are characterized by possessing a hinge with teeth and sockets that lock the two valves firmly together. Therefore these brachiopods are commonly found with both valves articulated.

Strophomena is a rather flat brachiopod with a straight hinge line. Usually more wide than long. Fine ribbing and faint growth lines present. Cosmopolitan. **Ordovician.**

Howellella is a small, triangular brachiopod with prominent pedicle valve. Up to eight very strong ribs. Cosmopolitan. **Silurian to Devonian.**

Leptaena is a thin shelled brachiopod with a straight hinge line and cup-shaped valves. The pedicle valve is convex, but the brachial valve is concave and sits inside the pedicle valve. There is a strong up-turn of the anterior margin in old individuals. **Ordovician to Devonian.**

Atrypa has convex valves, with the pedicle valve projecting slightly beyond the brachial valve. Ornament comprises fine growth lines and radial ribbing. General shape is circular with slightly flattened hinge area. Cosmopolitan. **Silurian to Devonian.**

Trigonorhynchia has strongly convex valves producing an almost spherical shell. A prominent sulcus is present on pedicle valve. Ribbing prominent. Pedicle foramen very small. Cosmopolitan. **Devonian,** but closely related forms range from the **Ordovician** to **Carboniferous.**

wellella

Strophomena

Atrypa

Leptaena

Trigonorhynchia

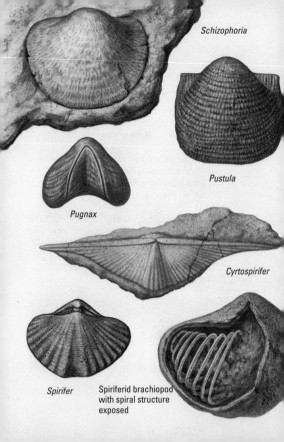

Schizophoria

Pustula

Pugnax

Cyrtospirifer

Spirifer

Spiriferid brachiopod
with spiral structure
exposed

Schizophoria has a strongly convex pedicle valve with a triangular callus and somewhat flat brachial valve. Shell generally smooth with faint ribbing and slightly elongate pustules. Cosmopolitan. **Silurian** to **Permian**.

Pugnax has a most elegant shell which is almost pyramidal in shape. The pedicle valve is flat posteriorly, but then sweeps into a deep, sharp sulcus. The brachial valve is highly inflated posteriorly, but anteriorly sweeps down to accommodate the sulcus. Ireland and UK. **Devonian** to **Carboniferous**.

Pustula has a highly inflated pedicle valve, flat or convex brachial valve and a straight hinge line. It is generally as wide as it is long. The ornament consists of prominent pustules and well developed growth lines. Cosmopolitan. **Lower Carboniferous**.

Spirifer is an elegant brachiopod with laterally extended valves, straight hinge line and prominent ribs. The brachidium is developed into a spiral structure which projects into the extended valves. Cosmopolitan. **Carboniferous**. Related forms survived until the **Jurassic**.

Cyrtospirifer is another brachiopod prized for its elegant shape. The hinge line is excessively extended and straight. Ribbing prominent as well as a ridge on the brachial valve. Highly compressed and distorted specimens from the Devonian of England are known as Delabole butterflies. **Devonian** to **Carboniferous**.

Productus is a relatively large brachiopod with convex pedicle valve, and flat or slightly convex brachial valve. Ornament consists of fine ribs and prominent growth lines. The pedicle valves had spines but these are often broken off. Cosmopolitan. **Carboniferous.**

Gigantoproductus is so called because of its enormous size. This brachiopod can reach a width of over 30 cm. Laterally extended valves, dome-shaped pedicle valve posteriorly. It has a series of strong ribs, often with fainter ribs superimposed. Cosmopolitan. **Lower Carboniferous.**

Horridonia is similar to *Productus*, but is adorned with elongate spines on the pedicle and brachial valves. These served to anchor the brachiopod in soft lime mud or shifting sands. Widespread in mainland Europe and County Durham in UK. **Permian.**

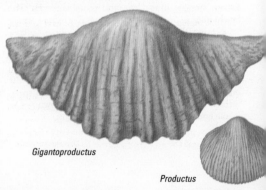

Gigantoproductus

Productus

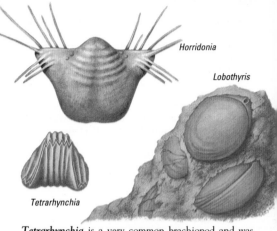

Horridonia

Lobothyris

Tetrarhynchia

Tetrarhynchia is a very common brachiopod and was widespread over most of Europe in the Lower Jurassic. It has a triangular outline, a small, hooked beak with a very small pedicle foramen. Both valves are strongly ribbed and a median sulcus is well developed. **Lower to Middle Jurassic.**

Lobothyris is a very smooth-shelled brachiopod with an almost straight commisure between the valves. Older specimens may show growth lines anteriorly. Common over most of Europe, but especially common in England, France, Germany and Spain. **Lower to Middle Jurassic.**

Torquirhynchia is an unusual brachiopod as it is not bilaterally symmetrical. Somewhat triangular outline with prominent ribs, the anterior margin is strongly offset diagonally. Common in England and France. **Upper Jurassic.**

Calcirhynchia is a small brachiopod, usually less than 1 cm diameter, with triangular outline, prominent sulcus and strong ribbing. Common in England. **Lower Jurassic.**

Terebrirostra is an unusual brachiopod in which the umbo is extended into a long tube projecting well beyond the main shell. Both valves convex, with prominent ribs. Western Europe. **Lower Cretaceous.**

Sellithyris is a smooth shelled brachiopod in which the anterior part of the shell is developed into a deep sulcus with a smooth keel within. This produces a letter M when viewed anteriorly. Common in Belgium, England, France and Switzerland. **Cretaceous.**

Terebratula has become a dumping ground for many smooth shelled, inflated brachiopods from the Mesozoic and Tertiary. Characterized by prominent umbonal region, rounded shape anteriorly, smooth valves. Usually two folds in anterior margin of brachial valve. The pedicle foramen is large. True *Terebratula* range from the **Miocene** to the **Pliocene.** The terebratulid group ranges from the **Jurassic** to **present day.**

Epithyris is a terebratulid with an almost circular outline with triangular umbonal region. Brachial valve becoming pentagonal in older individuals. Valves gently convex. Pedicle foramen large. Anterior margin developed into a series of gentle sulci and ridges in adult specimens. Growth lines also developed in adults. Cosmopolitan. **Jurassic.**

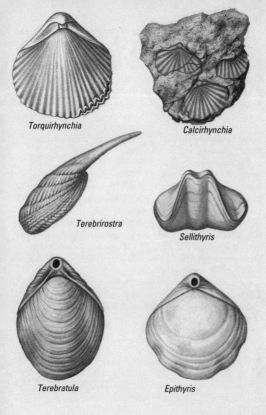

Torquirhynchia

Calcirhynchia

Terebrirostra

Sellithyris

Terebratula

Epithyris

MOLLUSCS

Molluscs are a diverse phylum of invertebrates whose fossil record goes back to the Lower Cambrian. Most classes of mollusc possess hard shells composed of calcite, aragonite or both, and therefore they have an excellent fossil record. The commonest fossil molluscs are the bivalves, gastropods and cephalopods. Other groups such as chitons and scaphopods are less well known, but may occur in abundance locally. The majority of molluscs are aquatic, with most being marine.

Bivalves have two shells, usually of equal size. They range in size from just a few millimetres to more than a metre. In some parts of the world they are important reef builders. Fossil bivalves are especially important as indicators of ancient marine environments.

Gastropods have become abundant in freshwater since the Carboniferous, and many gastropods are terrestrial. In most gastropods and cephalopods there is only a single shell, although these forms may have other mineralized parts such as jaws and opercula.

Cephalopods are particularly important because their relatively rapid rates of evolution and wide distribution make them important zone fossils. The cephalopod shell may be external, as in ammonites, or internal as in cuttlefish, squids and the fossil belemnites.

BIVALVES

Bivalves possess two calcareous shells, which are usually mirror images, although there are exceptions to this which are common as fossils. The shell may be composed of calcite, aragonite or both. The shells are joined anteriorly by a **ligament** and articulated by a **hinge** along which may be numerous **teeth** and **sockets**, and held together in life by strong adductor muscles which leave distinctive **muscle scars** inside the shell. The shell is secreted by the mantle, which also may leave a distinctive **pallial line** where it is attached to the shell. The shell may be smooth, or strongly ornamented with growth lines and radial ornament of ribs, spines and bullae. Modern bivalve shells are often brightly coloured, and fossil bivalves have been found with their original colour pattern. Bivalves are found in marine and fresh water. They may be shallow or deep burrowers, cementers on hard surfaces or attached by threads, or **byssus**. Some are free swimmers and a few fossil forms were planktonic.

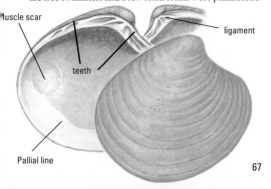

Muscle scar

ligament

teeth

Pallial line

Scallops

Entolium is a smooth-shelled scallop with regular but faint growth lines. The valves are almost equal with a straight hinge line. It has two almost symmetrical ears at the hinge. The anterior margin is semi-circular. Cosmopolitan. Triassic to Cretaceous.

Bositra is a thin-shelled scallop with a straight hinge line and prominent growth lines. It is often found as thousands of individuals covering bedding planes. Common in England, France, Germany and the Alps. Jurassic to Cretaceous. Closely related forms range from the Carboniferous to the Jurassic.

Bositra

Entolium

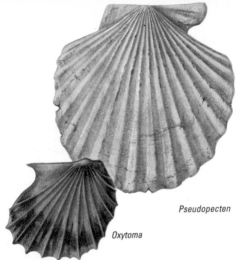

Pseudopecten

Oxytoma

Pseudopecten is a large scallop with slightly convex, equal valves, well developed ears at the hinge, one of which is extended to produce a notch. There are usually 15 or 16 prominent ribs which are often straight or only slightly curved. The margin is scalloped. Very common over most of Europe. Jurassic.

Oxytoma is a small scallop with straight hinge line and only one prominent ear. Ribbing is prominent and the margin is highly scalloped. The right valve is flat, the left valve convex. Cosmopolitan. Upper Triassic to Upper Cretaceous.

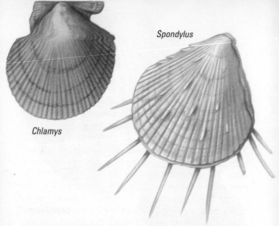

Spondylus

Chlamys

Chlamys is a genus that forms a large group of scallops with unequal ears, a large byssal notch and dense, fine to coarse ribbing. Imbricated growth lines are frequently prominent especially in adults. Cosmopolitan. Triassic to present day.

Spondylus is a small to medium sized oval-shaped scallop possessing elongate spines which help anchor it in soft lime ooze. Recent *Spondylus* often have irregular shells reflecting the surface over which they grow. Cosmopolitan. Jurassic to present day.

Oysters and oyster-like bivalves

Oysters are irregularly shaped bivalves, often with prominent, flared growth lines, and sometimes strong ribs. They usually cement one valve to a firm substrate, but may become free-lying as adults. They are very common as fossils, and may be found in extensive banks as are living oysters. *Gryphaea arcuata* is one of the commonest fossils in eastern and southern England. Commonly known as the Devil's Toenail, it has very thick shells composed of grey calcite. The robust nature of the shells allow it to be eroded out of cliffs on beaches and survive where other fossils are worn away. The umbonal region is rounded and incurved. The right valve is flat and sits like a small lid on the left valve. Growth lines are prominent. An elongate ridge is developed on the left valve. *Gryphaea* lived in soft mud, probably with only the margin exposed. Cosmopolitan. **Lower Jurassic.**

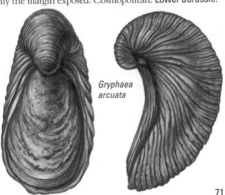

Gryphaea arcuata

*Gryphaea
(Bilobissa)*

Plicatula

Rastellum

Gryphaea (Bilobissa) is thinner shelled than *Gryphaea* from the Lower Jurassic, often reaching a larger size. It is wider, with a sub-circular outline. The right valve is strongly concave and sits within the left valve. Common in England, north France and Poland. **Middle** to **Upper Jurassic**.

Plicatula is a small flat scallop which can easily be confused with oysters. It has prominent growth rings and small plications or spines arranged radially. Cosmopolitan. **Triassic** to **present day**.

Rastellum is a distinctive oyster with high ribs and a zig-zag pattern at anterior margin. The shell is elongate and gently curved. Cosmopolitan. **Jurassic** to **Upper Cretaceous**.

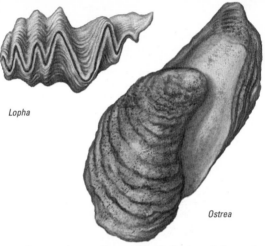

Lopha

Ostrea

Ostrea is the typical oyster. The shell is irregularly round or elongate reaching a length of over 20 cm. Growth lines are prominent. A single large muscle scar with growth lines is present internally. The ligament attachment scar is triangular, large and has numerous fine growth lines. Cosmopolitan. **Cretaceous** to present day.

Lopha is a highly irregular, fan-shaped oyster with strong ribs, some of which divide into two. Growth lines are usually faint, but some may be large representing interruptions to growth. Anterior margin with zig-zag pattern as in *Rastellum* (p. 72). Cosmopolitan. **Triassic** to present day.

Burrowing bivalves

Many bivalves burrow into soft sediment, often to considerable depth, and can be identified as burrowers by often having elongated shells, and a posterior indentation (**pallial sinus**) in the pallial line. Along the shell margin there may be one or two openings or **gapes**. A gape at the anterior is for the protrusion of a muscular **foot** used for burrowing, a gape at the posterior is for the accommodation of large **siphons** which extend to the surface of the burrow and are used for feeding. The valves are usually equal.

Pholadomya is a typical deep-burrowing bivalve, with an elongate and strongly convex shell. A gape is present. Ribbing is prominent with small notches, which assisted burrowing by providing a firm grip in the sediment. Cosmopolitan. **Upper Triassic** to **present day**.

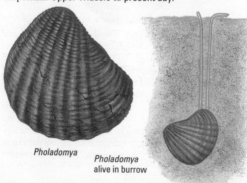

Pholadomya

Pholadomya
alive in burrow

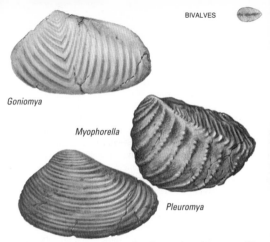

Goniomya

Myophorella

Pleuromya

Goniomya is a burrowing bivalve with a distinctive V-shaped pattern of ribs. There is a large gape for the siphons. Cosmopolitan. **Lower Jurassic to Eocene**.

Myophorella is a burrowing bivalve of triangular outline with curved margin. The surface is divided into two distinct patterns of ornament. The hind area has radial ribs, but the front region has prominent concentric growth lines or tubercles. Cosmopolitan. **Lower Jurassic to Lower Cretaceous**.

Pleuromya is a very common burrowing bivalve with moderately elongate shell. Shell smooth with faint concentric growth lines. Internal moulds show a deep sinus on the pallial line. Cosmopolitan. **Triassic to Lower Cretaceous**.

Other bivalves

Pinna has an elongate, triangular shell with ornament divided into two distinct regions and a large posterior gape. Half of shell usually with radial ribs, other half with concentric ribs or growth lines. Adult shells become smooth. Cosmopolitan. **Lower Carboniferous** to present day.

Modiolus is an elongate bivalve with straight hinge area, and small flexure in shell margin. Shells are strongly convex. Cosmopolitan. **Devonian** to present day.

Plagiostoma is a common bivalve, often up to 25 cm across. Mostly smooth, somewhat triangular outline with strongly convex shells. Cosmopolitan. **Triassic** to **Cretaceous**.

Inoceramus covers a large group of medium to large (over 1 m), often elongate bivalves with prominent concentric growth lines and ridges. Valves may be unequal, and usually lack radial ornament. Common in the chalk of northwest Europe. Was probably able to live on very soft sea floors. Cosmopolitan. **Jurassic** to **Cretaceous**.

Inoceramus

section
through shell

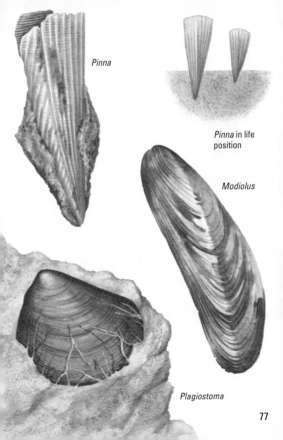

Pinna

Pinna in life position

Modiolus

Plagiostoma

77

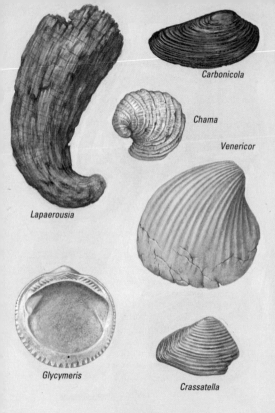

Carbonicola

Chama

Venericor

Lapaerousia

Glycymeris

Crassatella

Carbonicola is a small, smooth, biconvex, somewhat elongate bivalve. Lived in fresh or brackish water. Western Europe to Russia. **Upper Carboniferous.**

Lapaerousia belongs to a group of bivalves called rudists, which were abundant in Cretaceous times around the world in the tropics. They are characterized by strongly unequal valves. One valve is usually coiled in early life, becoming a straight cylinder later. The other valve becomes a 'lid' at the top of the cylinder. Some rudists reached over 1 m in length. France and Spain. **Upper Cretaceous.**

Venericor is a triangular, thick shelled, highly convex bivalve with prominent concentric growth lines and flat radial ribs separated by grooves. Cosmopolitan. **Palaeocene to Eocene.**

Chama is a highly distinctive, slightly coiled bivalve with convex valves. Ornament consists of flared concentric growth lines with spinose extensions. Cosmopolitan. **Palaeocene to present day.**

Glycymeris is an almost circular bivalve with faint radial striations. In the hinge area externally there is a V-shaped series of ridges and internally two series of numerous prominent teeth and sockets. There is a row of prominent crenulations on the anterior margin internally. Cosmopolitan. **Cretaceous to present day.**

Crassatella is a sub-rectangular to triangular bivalve with prominent concentric growth lines. Part of the shell slopes towards the posterior margin and may be smooth, or with faint growth lines. Anterior margin gently curved. Both valves are strongly convex. Cosmopolitan. **Cretaceous to Miocene.**

GASTROPODS

Gastropods are molluscs that have a single shell which is normally spiral, and in some forms, an **operculum** to close the **aperture**. Commonly the shell has a projecting **spire** constructed of earlier coils of the shell, each coil called a **whorl**. The commonest mode of coiling is to the right or **dextral**, but left hand or **sinistral** shells are known (see p. 87). The shells are often highly ornamented and some forms have apertures variously with teeth, spines, notches, or elongated into siphonal canals. As the shell grows, whorls may produce a central solid rod or **columella**, or surround an open space or **umbilicus.**

Gastropods may be marine, freshwater or terrestrial. They may be herbivores or carnivores and can reach sizes of several tens of centimetres. They are known from the Cambrian to Present, and are the most diverse group of molluscs today. Some living forms, such as slugs, do not have shells.

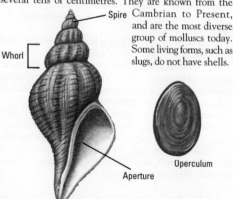

Spire

Whorl

Aperture

Operculum

Poleumita is a gastropod with a very low spire and large umbilicus. The upper whorl surface is ribbed and there may be a row of small studs or spines at the whorl margin. The lower surface may be smooth. The aperture is polygonal. Marine. Widespread in northwest Europe. Silurian.

Platyceras is a low-spired gastropod with rapidly expanding whorls. Shell is mostly smooth, but there is a groove on the upper surface of the last whorl and faint growth lines may be present. Marine. Cosmopolitan. Silurian to Middle Permian.

Bellerophon is one of the few gastropods that has a true planispiral shell, and may be confused at first glance with cephalopods, but note that it does not possess septa. The whorls are highly inflated and involute. There is a notch in the aperture which forms a band, or selenizone on earlier whorls. The aperture is flared in adults. Marine. Cosmopolitan. Silurian to Triassic.

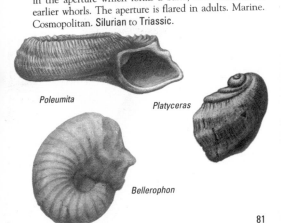

Poleumita

Platyceras

Bellerophon

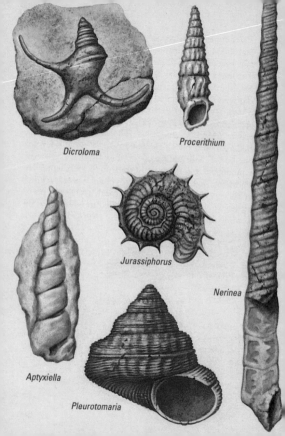

Dicroloma

Procerithium

Jurassiphorus

Aptyxiella

Nerinea

Pleurotomaria

Pleurotomaria is a common conical gastropod with a moderately high spire and overall triangular aspect. There is a slit on the aperture which becomes a selenizone on the whorl sides. Ornament of longitudinal and transverse ribs. Aperture square. Marine. **Jurassic to present day.**

Procerithium is a very common, small high-spired gastropod, which may occur as the major component of shell beds. The ornament comprises a series of spiral and transverse ribs or small tubercles. Marine. Cosmopolitan. **Jurassic.**

Nerinea belongs to an unusual group of gastropods with a very high spire which in some forms may be up to 1 m long. The aperture is smooth, but inside earlier whorls complex spiral ridges develop which give ornate, 'toothed' cross-sections. Common in limestones across Europe, abundant in France and Portugal where related forms commonly reached over 50 cm in length. Shallow marine. **Jurassic to Cretaceous.**

Aptyxiella is a high-spired gastropod, well known in England because of an unusual mode of preservation. On the Isle of Portland in Dorset *Aptyxiella* is preserved as moulds with no shell. As such it resembles a corkscrew in a hole and is locally known as the Portland Screw. Marine. **Upper Jurassic.**

Dicroloma is a small, elegant gastropod in which the aperture is extended into two or three elongate, gently curved spines and a siphonal canal. The spire is moderately high and whorls may have prominent ridges. Marine. **Jurassic.**

Jurassiphorus is a low-spired gastropod with spinose extensions along the whorl sides. The whorls have prominent ribs on the upper surface close to the spire suture. Marine. **Cretaceous.**

83

GASTROPODS

Turritella is a common, slender, extremely high-spired gastropod with 8 to 20 or more whorls, often with prominent, spiral ribs and faint growth lines. The aperture is rounded with a simple margin. Cosmopolitan. The family ranges from the Devonian to present day. Genus ranges from Oligocene to present day.

Natica is rather globular in overall shape. It has a wide aperture. The spire is low with a deep suture between adjacent whorls. There is a narrow umbilicus. *Natica* is a predatory gastropod which drills characteristic bevelled edged circular holes in bivalves. Palaeocene to present day.

Volutospina, also called *Athleta*, is an elegant gastropod with a moderately high, rather pointed spire and a large body whorl. It has prominent ribs each with a spine at the whorl shoulder. There are also a number of finer spiral ribs. Cretaceous to Pliocene.

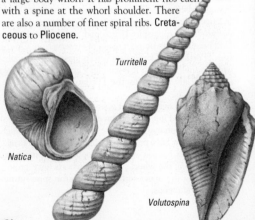

Turritella

Natica

Volutospina

Hippochrenes   *Clavilithes*

Hippochrenes is a large gastropod in which the whorl sides are smooth and flush to adjacent whorls. In adults the aperture has a large wing-like extension, and two prominent siphonal canals. Cosmopolitan. Eocene.

Clavilithes is another large gastropod reaching a total length of up to 25 cm. It has a moderate spire and an elongate siphonal canal. The suture between whorls is deep with an elevated border. Faint growth lines are usually visible on an otherwise smooth shell. Cosmopolitan. Palaeocene to Pliocene.

Tibia (see p. 86) is an elegant gastropod with a high spire and very elongate siphonal canal. Aperture has a folded lip. Ornament consists of both radial and transverse ribs. Marine. Cosmopolitan. Eocene.

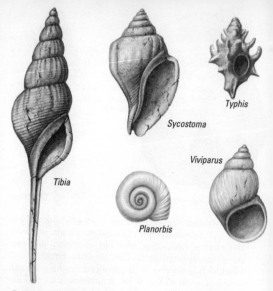

Tibia

Sycostoma

Typhis

Viviparus

Planorbis

Sycostoma is a gastropod with a large, high aperture with prominent callus where it laps onto previous whorl, and with a broad siphonal canal. Spire moderately high. Whorls smooth or with faint growth lines. Rather pear-shaped overall. Marine. Cosmopolitan. **Eocene.**

Typhis is a small, but nevertheless beautiful gastropod with numerous small hollow spines. The aperture is almost circular. Spire moderately high, with a small siphonal canal. Marine. Cosmopolitan. **Eocene.**

Viviparus is a freshwater gastropod of medium size with a rather globular aspect. The spire is relatively high with smooth convex whorls. Cosmopolitan. Jurassic to present day.

Planorbis is a freshwater gastropod with a discoidal shell. It is evolute, and usually smooth. The upper side of the shell may be almost flat, with an umbilicus below. Cosmopolitan. Jurassic to present day.

Neptunea despecta
dextral coiling

Neptunea contraria
sinistral coiling

Neptunea (above); two species of this high spired marine gastropod are shown to illustrate a dextral (coiled to the right) form and a sinistral (coiled to the left) form. Cosmopolitan. Both are from the Pleistocene.

SCAPHOPODS

Scaphopods are a distinct group of molluscs which have never been diverse, although they often occur in abundance. They are characterized by a gently curved, tapering shell, which is rather tusk-like in appearance. The shell is open at both ends and there may be a small slit at the narrow end. All are marine, and are known from the Devonian (possibly Ordovician) to the present day.
Dentalium is a typical scaphopod reaching a length of several centimetres. It has fine longitudinal ribs. Cosmopolitan. Triassic to present day.

CEPHALOPODS

Cephalopods are molluscs with a well-developed head, and a variable number of appendages or tentacles. Shells may be internal, external or absent, but when present are normally chambered. Shells are usually composed of aragonite, but some forms, notably belemnites, have calcite and aragonite. All cephalopods are marine.

Dentalium

Cephalopods with external shells were more diverse in the Palaeozoic and Mesozoic than they are today.

The shells are divided into a **body chamber**, which is occupied by the animal, and a chambered section, the **phragmocone**. Chambers, or **camarae** are separated by thin walls or **septa**, and are connected by a tube or **siphuncle**. This portion of the shell is used for buoyancy control like the air tanks in submarines. Where septa meet the shell wall a line is defined, the **septal suture**. The suture may be simple and straight as in many nautiloids, or convoluted and fern-like as in the ammonites. The suture pattern is an important aid for the identification of ammonites.

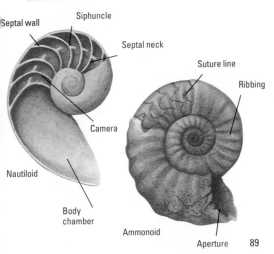

Septal wall

Siphuncle

Septal neck

Suture line

Ribbing

Camera

Nautiloid

Body chamber

Ammonoid

Aperture

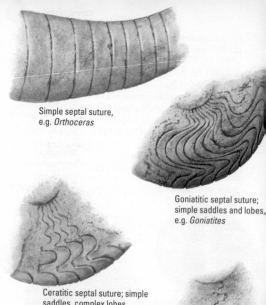

Simple septal suture,
e.g. *Orthoceras*

Goniatitic septal suture;
simple saddles and lobes,
e.g. *Goniatites*

Ceratitic septal suture; simple
saddles, complex lobes,
e.g. *Ceratites*

Highly complex
ammonitic septal
suture; highly complex
saddles and lobes,
e.g. *Phylloceras*

Ammonitic septal
suture; complex
saddles and lobes,
e.g. *Hildoceras*

Nautiloids

Nautiloids are cephalopods with a septate, external shell in which the siphuncle usually perforates the septal wall in the centre. The shell may be straight, gently curved or coiled in a tight planispiral. The suture is usually a simple straight or gently curved line. Some nautiloids reached gigantic proportions: up to 10 m. During Palaeozoic times nautiloids were very diverse, but only two or three species are alive today.

Cenoceras is a typical Mesozoic nautiloid with a highly involute planispiral shell, undulating sutures and a somewhat square outline to the aperture. Cosmopolitan. Nautiloids very similar to Cenoceras range from the **Triassic** to **present day**.

Cenoceras

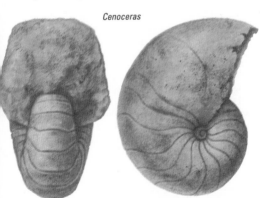

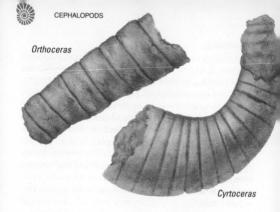

Orthoceras

Cyrtoceras

Orthoceras is a typical straight nautiloid with simple suture lines and a circular aperture. The overall shell shape is a very gently tapering cone. The ornament consists of very faint ribs. The chambers are strongly concave. *Orthoceras* may occur in abundance, with many specimens stacked within one another. Cosmopolitan. **Ordovician.** Straight shelled nautiloids similar to *Orthoceras* survived until the **Middle Triassic.**

Cyrtoceras is similar to *Orthoceras*, but the shell is gently curved like a cow's horns. The ornament consists of strong ribs. The siphuncle is placed towards the ventral surface which in *Cyrtoceras* is the outer side of the curve. Cosmopolitan. **Ordovician.**

Ammonoids

Ammonoids are a group of cephalopods which are mostly planispiral, with a few spectacular exceptions called the **heteromorphs**, some of which are shown on pp. 110-112. The siphuncle is almost always in a ventral position. The septal sutures are far more complex than in the nautiloids. In ammonoids the suture is divided into a series of **saddles** and **lobes**. These are relatively simple in the earlier goniatites, but they become more complex in the Mesozoic forms, especially ammonites. The Triassic ceratites developed rather crenulated lobes, and this was taken to extremes by the ammonites which developed highly intricate fern-like patterns on both the saddles and lobes. Ammonoids, like all cephalopods, were fully marine and tend not to be found in sediments deposited in inshore environments. Their shells were made entirely of aragonite, but some forms had calcitic jaws called **aptychi** (see p.105). Ammonoids are among the most useful of fossils for biostratigraphic purposes, especially in Mesozoic rocks.

Many Jurassic and Cretaceous forms show marked changes in ornamentation through life, with some having strongly ribbed early whorls, but smooth adult body chambers. Differences between sexes occur in adult shells in many species with shells thought to be of females (**macroconchs**) being much larger than those of the males (**microconchs**, see p. 104). The shells of the males sometimes have the aperture modified with projections or spines.

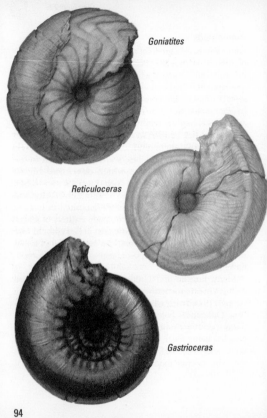

Goniatites

Reticuloceras

Gastrioceras

94

Goniatitids

Goniatitids are ammonoids that appeared in the Devonian and flourished until the end of the Permian when they became extinct. They are characterized by rather globular, involute shells, all with goniatitic sutures. They have been used widely in Europe and the USA for correlating marine strata within Carboniferous coal bearing sequences.

Goniatites itself is perhaps the most characteristic of the group as a whole. It is highly involute, with a small, almost circular umbilicus. The suture has a simple, sharply pointed saddle and lobe on each side, and a saddle where the suture crosses over the venter giving it a zig-zag appearance. The shell is smooth with faint growth lines. Cosmopolitan. **Lower Carboniferous.**

Reticuloceras is slightly more evolute than *Goniatites*. It is globular with faint sinuous growth lines and longitudinal ridges giving a reticulated pattern. Cosmopolitan. **Upper Carboniferous.**

Gastrioceras is relatively evolute for a goniatite. It has well-developed ribs or nodes on the lower side of the whorl close to the umbilicus, but these fade towards the ventral margin. At approximately quarter whorl intervals there are narrow constrictions of the shell. Cosmopolitan. **Upper Carboniferous.**

Ammonites

Ammonoids continued to evolve after a great extinction event wiped out almost all of the externally shelled cephalopods at the end of the Permian. The ceratites flourished during the Triassic, but these too were extinct by the end of the Triassic.

Just two groups survived into the Jurassic and radiated to produce the ammonites, perhaps the most diverse group of all the cephalopods. During the early Jurassic a group of ammonites known as the phyloceratids gave rise to another important group, the lytoceratids, which in turn gave rise to all other ammonites.

The lytoceratids were evolute, simple ribbed ammonites of which **Lytoceras** is typical. *Lytoceras* has a circular aperture and simple, straight ribs. Every few centimetres it produced a more prominent rib, which in some species was a recurved, horseshoe-shaped collar. Cosmopolitan. *Lytoceras* and closely related forms range from the **Jurassic** to **Cretaceous**.

Lytoceras

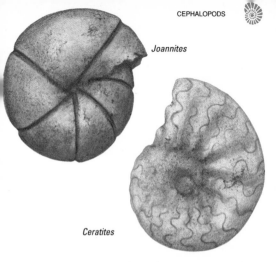

Joannites

Ceratites

Joannites is an extremely involute ammonite in which the whorls entirely overlap preceding whorls such that early whorls are wholly obscured. The shell is smooth with regular constrictions. The suture is ammonitic. Common in the Alpine region. **Triassic.**

Ceratites flourished during the Triassic, but is unknown in the UK. The most characteristic feature is the ceratitic suture pattern (see p. 93). *Ceratites* is a moderately evolute ammonite with a square aperture. Ribs are prominent and well spaced. Widespread in southern Europe, including the Alps and southern Germany. **Triassic.**

Psiloceras

Psiloceras is a highly evolute ammonite with a low expansion rate. Cross-section of whorl oval. The outer whorls are usually devoid of ornament. *Psiloceras* is the earliest ammonite to be found in Jurassic rocks in the UK. Common over most of northwest Europe. **Lower Jurassic.**

Schlotheimia has a laterally compressed whorl cross-section, well-developed ribs and is moderately evolute. There is a well-developed groove on the ventral margin. Cosmopolitan. **Lower Jurassic.**

Schlotheimia

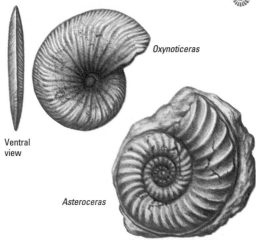

Ventral
view

Oxynoticeras

Asteroceras

Oxynoticeras is highly compressed laterally, with the whorl sides culminating in a sharp keel over the ventral margin. Ribbing may be developed which is curved forward slightly at the umbilical margin. Highly involute. Cosmopolitan. **Lower Jurassic.**

Asteroceras is an evolute ammonite with prominent large ribs which are slightly curved towards the aperture. There is a keel on the ventral margin with a groove on either side. This ammonite is famous for its beautiful state of preservation on the English south coast. Cosmopolitan. **Lower Jurassic.**

Harpoceras is a moderately involute ammonite which is laterally compressed with a prominent keel and flat whorl sides. The ribs are sickle-shaped, markedly curving forwards as they approach the ventral margin. Adult specimens may reach a diameter of 50 cm. There are several closely related genera such as *Tiltoniceras*, *Hildaites* and *Protogrammoceras* (see p. 18). Cosmopolitan, but especially common in Yorkshire, UK and southern Germany. **Lower Jurassic.**

Harpoceras

Dactylioceras

Hildoceras

Dactylioceras is a very common evolute ammonite with almost circular whorl cross-section. Prominent ribs often splitting into two before they pass over the ventral margin. Some related forms may have tubercles. The body chamber makes up almost one full whorl. Cosmopolitan. **Lower Jurassic.**

Hildoceras is closely related to *Harpoceras*, but has a rather more square whorl cross-section, is more evolute and has three keels on the ventral margin. The ribbing is sickle-shaped, but part of the whorls side is smooth, with no ribs. Evolute. Cosmopolitan. **Lower Jurassic.**

Both *Dactylioceras* and *Hildoceras* occur commonly on the Yorkshire coast around Whitby. *Hildoceras* takes its name from St. Hilda who is said to have rid Whitby of a plague of snakes by turning them into stone. Local people sometimes carve snake heads onto the body chambers of both these ammonites.

Phylloceras

Septal suture
pattern

Phylloceras is one of the most beautiful of the European
ammonites. It is laterally compressed and highly involute,
with none of the early whorls being visible. It has a rapid
whorl expansion, and may become very large. The body
wall is smooth, with faint growth lines. The suture lines
are highly characteristic, being a very complex pattern of
fern-like saddles and lobes. Cosmopolitan. Lower Jurassic to Lower Cretaceous.

Macrocephalites

Macrocephalites is a large, highly involute ammonite, with only a small portion of the early whorls being visible. The whorls are often wider than they are high, producing very fat, almost globular shells. Ribbing is simple, but strongly developed. Cosmopolitan. **Middle Jurassic.**

Cadoceras is even more involute and globular than *Macrocephalites* above. The overall shell shape being rather cannon ball-like. The shell is frequently strongly ribbed but the body chamber of adult macroconchs is usually smooth (see p. 104). Common through northwest and central Europe to Russia. **Middle Jurassic.**

Cadoceras

Kosmoceras is slightly involute with square whorl cross-section. A row of tubercles on the ribs at the point where they cross the ventral margin accentuates the squareness. The ribs split repeatedly midway on the whorl side. There is often a tubercle at this point. Common through north-west and central Europe to Russia. **Middle Jurassic.**

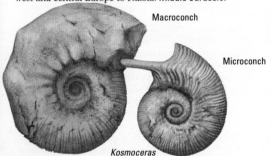

Macroconch

Microconch

Kosmoceras

Macroconchs and microconchs

Adult ammonite shells often exhibit strong differences on the last whorl. Some forms grew large, highly inflated last whorls, and are known as **macroconchs,** others remained relatively small, but grew some sort of modification of the shell margin. These forms are called **microconchs.** They may have lateral extensions of the aperture called **lappets** as in the microconch of *Kosmoceras.* It is believed that microconchs were male and macroconchs female. The younger whorls of the shells of corresponding macroconchs and microconchs are usually indistinguishable.

Perisphinctes belongs to a large group of common ammonites, the early whorls of which are similar to *Dactylioceras* from the Lower Jurassic, but the perisphinctids grew much larger. In the genus *Perisphinctes* the ribs are straight, splitting into two or three as they pass over the ventral margin. Many forms show a change in ribbing pattern as they reached adult size. Cosmopolitan. **Upper Jurassic.**

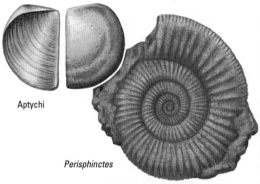

Aptychi

Perisphinctes

Aptychi are paired shell-like structures which ammonites used as jaws or as opercula to close the shell. They are usually made of calcite or a tough organic material. They are only commonly preserved when made of calcite. They are only rarely found inside the ammonite, having dropped out of the shell when the ammonite died. They can easily be mistaken for the shells of bivalves, but note that they do not have teeth, ligament pits or muscle scars.

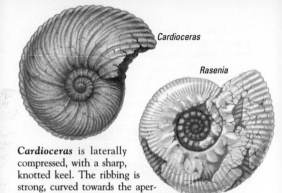

Cardioceras

Rasenia

Cardioceras is laterally compressed, with a sharp, knotted keel. The ribbing is strong, curved towards the aperture and splits into two or three. Additional ribs may be inserted between the splitting ribs. Europe through to Russia. **Upper Jurassic.**

Rasenia belongs to the perisphinctid group of ammonites. English specimens are famous for their good preservation, often showing the original mother of pearl lustre. Ribs are developed over the ventral margin with plications on the whorl side. Moderately involute. North Europe to Russia. **Upper Jurassic.**

Titanites is also a perisphinctid ammonite, and is one of the largest of the European ammonites, reaching a diameter of over 1 m. Strongly ribbed, but body chamber becomes smooth in adults. Common on the Dorset coast, but because of its size it is difficult to collect. May be seen used as an ornamental stone in gardens in southern England. Also found in north France and possibly Russia. **Upper Jurassic.**

Titanites

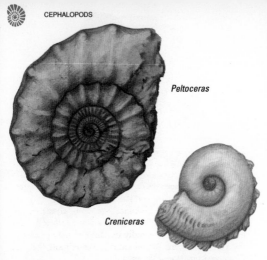

Peltoceras

Creniceras

Peltoceras is an evolute perisphinctid ammonite of which very young specimens are almost indistinguishable from *Perisphinctes*, but as adults, *Peltoceras* develops very strong spines on thick ribs at the ventral margin and on the whorl sides. Whorl cross-section is square in adults. May grow to over 50 cm diameter. Cosmopolitan. **Middle Jurassic.**

Creniceras is a small, laterally compressed ammonite with smooth whorl sides. It is distinctive because of a row of crenulations on the ventral margin, giving it a 'saw tooth' keel. Microconchs with lappets. Cosmopolitan. **Upper Jurassic.**

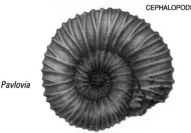

Pavlovia

Pavlovia is an evolute ammonite with prominent ribs which split into two or three as they pass over the ventral margin. *Pavlovia* often exhibits constrictions of the whorls in larger specimens. May reach over 50 cm diameter. England, north France and Russia. **Upper Jurassic.**

Virgatosphinctes is an evolute ammonite characterized by ribs which bifurcate in young specimens, trifurcate and eventually branch repeatedly in adults as they pass over the ventral margin. Whorl cross-section almost circular. Cosmopolitan. **Upper Jurassic.**

Virgatosphinctes

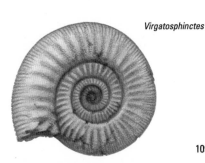

CEPHALOPODS

Hoplites

Hoplites is a distinctive, moderately evolute ammonite with prominent ribs that curve forwards slightly at the ventral margin, becoming raised into ventro-lateral tubercles on older individuals. There is a deep sulcus on the venter. Cosmopolitan. **Lower Cretaceous.**

A number of ammonoids are irregularly coiled, or are regularly coiled but in a non-planispiral fashion, and are known as **heteromorphs**. They occur sporadically from the Devonian to the Cretaceous.

Turrilites resembles a high spired gastropod in its coiling mode, but is distinguished from gastropods by the presence of typical ammonitic sutures and chambered shell. Cosmopolitan. **Cretaceous.**

Turrilites

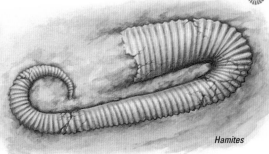

Hamites

Hamites and several closely related genera are heteromorph ammonites in which the shell coils in an open fashion, usually with three sub-parallel, straight sections. The early whorls may be helically coiled. *Hamites* is strongly ribbed, but the ribs are not present on the dorsal side. The whorl cross-section is usually circular. Particularly well-preserved specimens are common in the Gault Clay of the Kent coast at Folkestone, England, where the original shell is preserved and displays a brilliant pink mother of pearl lustre. Many heteromorph ammonites reached a large size, some forms closely related to *Hamites* frequently reached a length of more than 1 m. Cosmopolitan. **Cretaceous.**

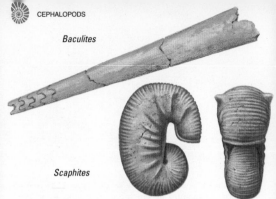

Baculites

Scaphites

Baculites is an almost straight ammonite, with only the very earliest part of the shell being coiled. Some forms may be slightly curved. Some specimens may reach lengths of over 2 m, but large specimens are often broken, probably due to predation by large marine reptiles such as mosasaurs and pliosaurs (see p.189). Distinguished from similar shaped orthoconic nautiloids by presence of complex suture pattern. Cosmopolitan. **Cretaceous.**

Scaphites is a heteromorph ammonite which begins coiling like an ordinary ammonite, but then straightens its shell for a short period. It then begins to coil again so that the aperture is facing the earlier coiled part of the shell. It is usually strongly ribbed, but in adult individuals the ribbing on the body chamber is usually more bold and widely spaced than that on the phragmocone and may be tuberculate. Cosmopolitan. **Cretaceous.**

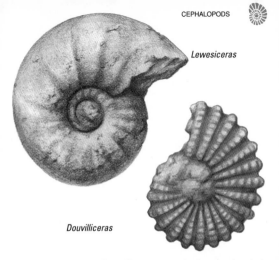

Lewesiceras

Douvilliceras

Lewesiceras is a laterally compressed, planispiral coiled ammonite, remarkable because of its size, specimens almost reaching 1 m diameter. Early whorls are ribbed with lateral tubercles on early whorls, becoming smooth on later whorls. Cosmopolitan. **Upper Cretaceous.**

Douvilliceras is a very coarsely ribbed ammonite in which the ribs have numerous small tubercles giving a pattern resembling the tread of a car tyre. A sulcus is developed on the ribs at the ventral margin. Somewhat involute, a rather globular shell shape with rounded to slightly polygonal whorl section. Cosmopolitan. **Lower Cretaceous.**

Belemnites

Belemnites were squid-like cephalopods, with an internal skeleton comprising a heavy **guard** made of radiating crystals of calcite with a conical chambered shell, the **phragmocone**, composed of aragonite which was sited anteriorly within an **alveolus**. There was a long anterior extension of the phragmacone, the **proostracum**, but this is not often preserved. The belemnite animal had tentacles with many small **hooklets** composed of a tough organic material. Some forms had a pair of larger hooks used in mating, and many forms possessed an ink sac. The guard is the commonest part of belemnites found fossilized, often occurring in huge numbers known as belemnite battlefields. They were fully marine, common in the Mesozoic, and can be used as biostratigraphic indicators (see p. 15). Species are distinguished by the overall shape and position of longitudinal grooves on the guard surface. **Growth lines** can be seen in the guard when broken.

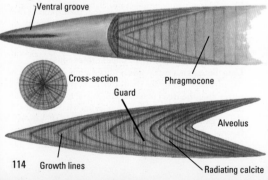

Ventral groove

Cross-section

Phragmocone

Guard

Alveolus

Radiating calcite

Growth lines

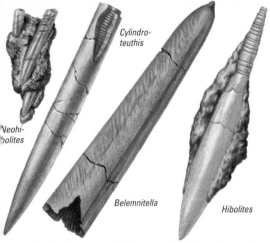

Cylindro-teuthis

Neohi-bolites

Belemnitella

Hibolites

Neohibolites is a small belemnite, slightly flared anteriorly. Cosmopolitan. **Lower Cretaceous**.

Cylindroteuthis has a large, elegantly tapered, sharply pointed guard reaching a length of 20 cm. Prominent ventral groove developed. Widespread in northwest Europe. Very common in the Oxford Clay of central England. **Jurassic**.

Belemnitella is characterized by a small tubercle at the tip of the guard. Most of northwest Europe. **Upper Cretaceous**.

Hibolites is elegantly tapered and flared anteriorly to accommodate the phragmacone. This part is often broken, making the guard appear pointed at both ends. Cosmopolitan. **Jurassic** to **Lower Cretaceous**.

ANNELIDS

Annelids are bilaterally symmetrical segmented worms and include the familiar earthworms. Most forms are aquatic, with many marine annelids secreting calcareous skeletons which are easily preserved as fossils. Indeed some annelids were so abundant that their tubes can be a major component of some limestones, and are known to form small reefs in the Jurassic of southern Germany.

Serpula is an encrusting annelid with a calcitic tube which often shows faint growth lines. Some species are characterized by flanges running the length of the tube.

Serpula is commonly found cemented to large oysters and ammonites. Cosmopolitan. **Silurian to present day.**

Genicularia is a worm tube with bulbous ribs and a square cross-section. Cosmopolitan. **Jurassic to Cretaceous.**

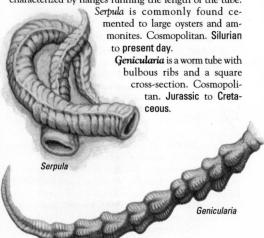

Serpula

Genicularia

116

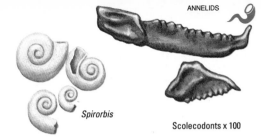

ANNELIDS

Spirorbis

Scolecodonts x 100

Spirorbis is a small spiral worm tube coiled in a flat plane which may be found cemented to firm substrates. Some specimens may show fine concentric ridges. Ordovician to present day.

Scolecodonts are the teeth of predatory annelid worms. They are made of tough organic materials which preserve readily in the fossil record. They are usually microscopic, and are often the only clue to the fossil record of annelids that did not posses calcareous tubes. Not all annelids possessed scolecodonts.

Oyster encrusted with *Serpula*

ARTHROPODS

Arthropods are bilaterally symmetrical animals with jointed, external skeletons, and include crabs, lobsters, wood lice, insects, king crabs, spiders and scorpions. In addition to these familiar living animals there are many bizarre and wonderful fossil arthropods that are now extinct, the most important group of which are the trilobites. Arthropods vary in size from microscopic, even when adult, to the enormous giant crabs with limb-tip to limb-tip diameters of over 2 m.

Some arthropods have skeletons which are mineralized by calcite or apatite (calcium phosphate), both of which preserve well and as such are common as fossils. All arthropods have to repeatedly shed their exoskeletons by **ecdysis**, which means that one individual can contribute many skeletal elements to the fossil record. Isolated pieces of shed skeletons of arthropods are much more common than complete articulated skeletons.

Trilobites

Trilobites are arthropods which appeared in the Lower Cambrian and became extinct by the end of the Permian. They were fully marine, possibly predatory, and some had the ability to enroll like pill wood lice. Some forms were blind, possibly living in deep water, but most forms were shallow water dwellers. They range in size from only a few millimetres to several tens of centimetres in length.

The trilobite skeleton was segmented, calcitic, and divided into three main regions; a head or **cephalon,** a body or **thorax** and a tail or **pygidium**. The cephalon is further divided into segments, the most visible of which are the **compound eyes** and a **free cheek** bordered by a **facial suture**. In addition there is a raised central area called the **glabella**. The free cheek may be extended posteriorly into a **genal spine**. The thorax is divided into many small segments called **pleura** which allow the trilobite to coil up. There is a prominent central **axis** running from the glabella to the pygidium. A few trilobites are known with their soft parts preserved and these show they had numerous limbs and gills beneath the thorax, and some forms had long antennae.

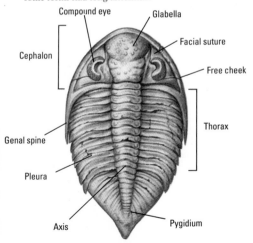

Compound eye — Glabella

Cephalon

Facial suture

Free cheek

Genal spine

Thorax

Pleura

Axis

Pygidium

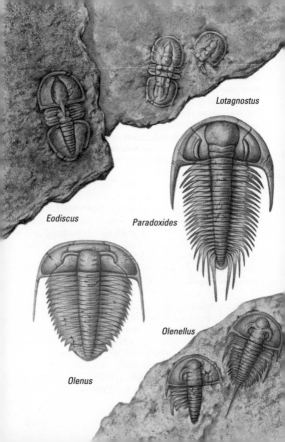

Lotagnostus

Eodiscus

Paradoxides

Olenus

Olenellus

One group of trilobites, the **agnostids**, were blind and had a head shield very similar to the tail segment. These might have been deep water forms. They usually have only two or three pleural segments in the thorax and are common in marine Lower Palaeozoic rocks, especially dark coloured shales.

Lotagnostus has only two pleural segments. The glabella is somewhat smaller than the axis in the pygidium. There are two small spines on the pygidium which has a number of small radiating furrows. North Europe. **Upper Cambrian.**

Eodiscus is another agnostid trilobite and is easily recognized by a posterior pointing spine on a short glabella and a segmented axis in the pygidium. There are three pleural segments. Usually up to 1 cm in length. **Middle Cambrian.**

Paradoxides is a spectacular trilobite in which the cephalon has two large genal spines. The thorax is long with 16-21 pleural segments. The posterior pleural segments are spinose. The pygidium is very small with a square posterior margin. Sweden and Scotland. **Middle Cambrian.**

Olenus is a broad trilobite with prominent genal spines and a glabella with six small furrows. The thorax may have 13-15 pleural segments, and is followed by a small, triangular pygidium sometimes with very small spines. Widespread in Europe. **Upper Cambrian.**

Olenellus is an elongate, spinose trilobite up to 4 cm in length. Cephalon with two small genal spines, smooth glabella and prominent, arcuate eyes. Third pleura of the thorax extended to produce spines. Pygidium elongated to produce a tail spine almost as half as long as the complete animal. Scotland. **Lower Cambrian.**

121

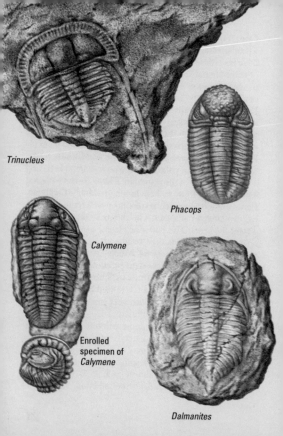

Trinucleus

Phacops

Calymene

Enrolled
specimen of
Calymene

Dalmanites

Trinucleus is a very distinctive trilobite with a broad area in front of the glabella which is covered in sensory pits or grooves. There are two spectacularly long genal spines and the glabella is very high and bulbous. There are only six pleura in the thorax and the pygidium is short. Common in the UK, Norway and Sweden. **Ordovician.**

Phacops is an elongate trilobite with large compound eyes and a bulbous glabella. There is no genal spine and the pleural segments are rounded at their tips. The pygidium is small. Total length about 4 cm. Cosmopolitan. **Silurian.**

Calymene is similar to *Phacops* but is generally larger. The thorax has 13 segments and the pygidium six rings. *Calymene* could roll up and clip the pygidium to the head-shield as protection against predators. This trilobite is common in the Silurian Wenlock Limestone of England where specimens are known as Dudley locusts. **Silurian to Devonian.**

Dalmanites is an elegantly streamlined trilobite in which long genal spines are flush with the thorax. The pygidium tapers to a sharp, elongate point and has a number of sinuous grooves on its surface. There are small tubercles on the axis in the thorax. Cosmopolitan. **Silurian.**

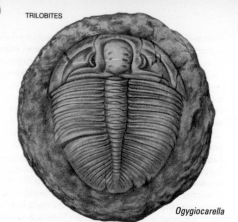

Ogygiocarella

Ogygiocarella is a relatively large trilobite with an oval outline. The cephalon is divided into two by a large glabella with eight furrows. The eyes are lunate and set well back. The free cheeks are smooth. The division between the thorax in the pygidium is indistinct in articulated specimens, but there is a marked tapering of the thorax at the pygidium margin. There are furrows on the pygidium which are continuous with the pleura. This is a very common trilobite in Ordovician rocks of the Welsh borders region of England. Several closely related genera occur in northern Europe. **Middle Ordovician.**

Encrinuroides and *Encrinurus* are two small but never-theless spectacular trilobites which are closely related. The cephalon is highly distinctive with an inflated gla-bella covered with tubercles. The cheeks behind the eyes are also tuberculate. In some species the eyes are raised on short stalk-like processes. Prominent genal spines present which are long in some forms. The axis on the pygidium is segmented with a row of centrally placed tubercles, as well as two rows of tubercles lateral to the axis. Cosmo-politan. Ordovician to Silurian.

Leonaspis is a spinose trilobite in which all of the pleura are extended into posterior pointing spines and a number of spines are developed on the pygidium, two of which are elongated. In addition there is a row of short forward facing spines on the anterior margin of the cephalon. The genal spines are also well developed. Cosmopolitan. Silu-rian to Lower Devonian.

Leonaspis

Encrinuroides

125

Asaphellus is a trilobite with an oval outline. The pygidium and cephalon have a similar size and shape and are generally smooth. Genal spines are developed as a continuation of an anterior platform running around the front of the cephalon, and a similar platform runs around the posterior margin of the pygidium. The glabella is smooth, and broad posteriorly. There are eight pleural segments in the adult. England and Wales. **Ordovician.**

Harpes is a beautiful trilobite with a high glabella, a horseshoe-shaped margin to the cephalon with greatly extended genal spines. Cephalon with numerous tubercles, thorax has 29 segments. The genal spines may have supported the animal on soft ground. Cosmopolitan. **Silurian to Devonian.**

Flexicalymene is a very similar trilobite to *Calymene* (p. 122) but the thorax has only 12 or 13 segments. Like *Calymene* this trilobite could roll up for protection. Cosmopolitan. Specimens of Calymene or closely related genera from Morocco are commonly found for sale in fossil shops. **Ordovician.**

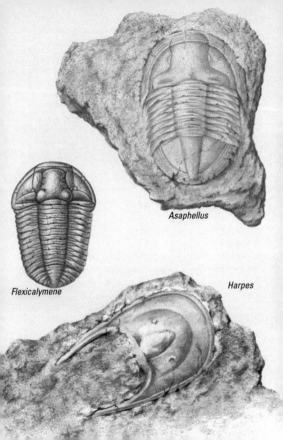

Asaphellus

Flexicalymene

Harpes

CRUSTACEANS

Crustaceans are the most abundant of the aquatic arthropods today, and are a major component of modern marine food webs. They include the microscopic ostracods and copepods, the familiar barnacles, crabs and lobsters, as well as a few terrestrial forms such as wood lice. They have a distinct head, thorax and abdomen. There are five **appendages** on the head which are usually involved in feeding and for sensory purposes. The thorax and abdomen also have appendages which are usually used for locomotion.

Only the barnacles, ostracods and some of the malacostraca (crabs and lobsters) have mineralized exoskeletons, and as such only these groups are common as fossils. The fossil record of crustaceans ranges from the Cambrian to present day.

Barnacles

Barnacles or cirripedes are the familiar objects found encrusting rocks in the intertidal zone and the bottoms of boats. Some forms bore into rocks (see p. 234), some are parasitic, while others produce large calcitic skeletons cemented to firm substrates. Isolated plates of barnacles may be more common than complete individuals. The fossil record of barnacle goes back to the Silurian.

Balanus is a common fossil form from the **Pleistocene** of Europe which cements to firm substrates.

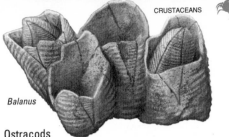

Balanus

Ostracods

Ostracods are small bivalved crustaceans with calcitic valves, commonly only 1 mm long, although a few Cambrian forms were up to 20 mm long. Ostracods shed their valves as they grow and leave distinctive **instars**. They can be so common as fossils as to make ostracod limestone. There are many hundreds of different genera, and they are common in marine and freshwater sediments ranging from the Cambrian to the present day. They are frequently used in biostratigraphy and for estimating ancient water salinities. You require a good hand lens to recognize ostracods in the field as they can be confused with oolitic limestone.

Patagonacythere x 20, a
highly ornamented ostracod

Ostracod limestone

129

Conchostracans

Conchostracans are crustaceans with bivalved carapaces which resemble small bivalved molluscs. The shell may be organic or composed of calcium phosphate. Unlike ostracods, conchostracans grow their shells by continuously adding new growth rings. Conchostracans are typically 5-10 mm long, and often found as mass mortality accumulations where hundreds of individuals cover bedding surfaces. Modern conchostracans live mainly in fresh water.

Euestheria is found in the English Triassic, but there are many other forms from the Jurassic of Scotland and Cretaceous of southern England. Conchostracans are found all over the world ranging from the **Devonian** to **present day**.

Mass mortality of conchostracans

Euestheria x 4

Crabs, lobsters and shrimps

Mecochirus is a shrimp-like crustacean with prominent elongate forelimbs or **pereipods.** Typically the body is only 2 or 3 cm in length, but the limbs extend several centimetres. The carapace is very thin. *Mecochirus* is relatively common in fine grained limestones and shales and has been found in England and Germany. **Middle and Upper Jurassic.**

Waterstonella is a small, shrimp-like crustacean often found as mass mortality assemblages. Well known in organic rich shales of the Midland Valley of Scotland, but rare elsewhere. **Carboniferous.**

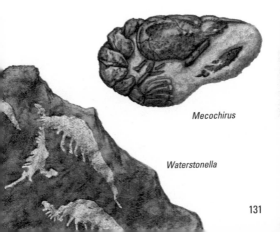

Mecochirus

Waterstonella

Eryon is a crab-like crustacean with a broad thorax and a short abdomen. There is a flared tail region composed of four lateral plates and a short central spike or **telson**. The anterior limbs bear fine grasping claws. The thorax is roughly pentagonal in outline and the anterior margin has small spines. The best specimens come from exceptional deposits such as the Solnhofen Limestone and the Posidonia Shale, both in southern Germany, but fragments of *Eryon* are not rare elsewhere. **Jurassic** to **Cretaceous.**

Eryon

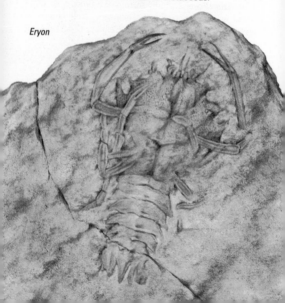

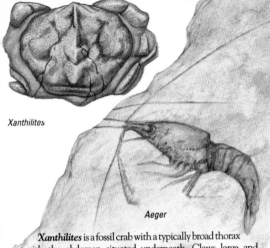

Xanthilites

Aeger

Xanthilites is a fossil crab with a typically broad thorax with the abdomen situated underneath. Claws large and conspicuous. Fossil crabs, lobsters and shrimps are often found on beaches having been washed out of Tertiary clays where they are commonly preserved in phosphatic nodules. There are many species of fossil crab in the Tertiary rocks of Europe. **Palaeocene to Middle Eocene.**

Aeger is a typical shrimp; the first three pairs of legs modified for feeding, and five pairs of thoracic limbs used for walking. The antennae are long and there is a long pointed rostrum anteriorly. There are many types of fossil shrimp, which are common throughout Europe from the Jurassic to the present day. Range of *Aeger* **Triassic to Jurassic.**

133

CHELICERATES

The chelicerates are a diverse group of arthropods ranging from the Cambrian to the present day. They include spiders, mites, scorpions, the living king crabs and the extinct eurypterids. All have a pair of pincers called **chelicerae** and a head shield comprising a fused head and thorax known as the **prosoma**. The skeleton is rarely mineralized, and as such chelicerates are rare as fossils. King crabs are known from the Solnhofen Limestone (Jurassic) of Bavaria (see p. 237) and the related *Euproops* is known from the Upper Carboniferous of England.

Euproops

Eurypterus

Eurypterids are scorpion-like chelicerates adapted to an aquatic existence. They had a large prosoma and a segmented body. Most species possessed a long pointed telson at the tail. Two limbs were modified as paddles for swimming. They were major predators during the Ordovician and Silurian, but became extinct by the end of the Permian. They reached a length of almost 2 m and occurred in both marine and freshwater. Exceptionally well preserved eurypterids are known from Scotland and the Baltic states.

ECHINODERMS

The echinoderms include the sea urchins, starfishes, brittle stars, sea cucumbers and sea lilies, and are a diverse group of entirely marine organisms. They are united by the possession of an **internal skeleton** composed of plates of calcite with a distinctive microstructure known as **stereom**. The skeleton may consist of isolated spicules (similar to those of some sponges), numerous articulated plates or numerous plates fused into a box-like **test** or **theca**. The internal anatomy is dominated by a mouth and an anus with a simple gut. Locomotion is by means of tube feet kept rigid by hydrostatic pressure. There is no distinct head. A remarkable feature of most echinoderms is a five fold (**pentameral**) symmetry, although in many forms this is somewhat obscured by a bilateral symmetry. A conspicuous series of plates with small paired holes arranged in rows of five 'petals' are known as the **ambulacra**.

Echinoderms first appeared in the Cambrian and underwent several rapid bursts of evolution. A number of formerly important classes of echinoderms have become extinct, but five classes are alive today. Of these, the sea urchins and the starfishes are the most important and diverse. Isolated plates and spines of echinoderms are very abundant as fossils, as are almost complete tests of those with fused skeletons.

Fossil echinoderms occupied a wide range of habitats, including free swimming planktonic forms, burrowers, cementers, and forms which crawled along the sea bed. Some forms were detritus feeders, some filter feeders, and some starfish were active hunters preying on bivalves and small fish.

Calcichordates

Calcichordates are an extinct group of unusual echinoderms that are believed to be related to the chordates.
They do not possess the five fold symmetry of the other
echinoderms, but they do have internal skeletons composed of calcite plates with typical stereom. As they are
extinct it has been difficult to determine the function of
the various parts of the skeleton, and even distinguishing
the mouth from the anus has proved to be difficult in some
forms. *Cothurnocystis* is from the **Ordovician**
of Scotland and *Placocystites* is from
the **Silurian** of England and Sweden. All were extinct by
the middle of the
Devonian.

Placocystites (left) &
Cothurnocystis

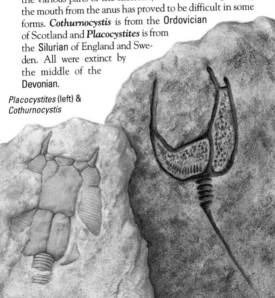

Blastoids

Blastoids are an extinct group of stalked echinoderms with a small theca composed of triangular and diamond-shaped plates arranged in three rings of five. The ambulacra are petal-like. They range from the Silurian to the Permian and may be common in some limestones. Some are very small and can easily be overlooked.

Deltoblastus from the **Permian** of southeast Asia is a beautiful form with a flower-like series of basal plates of the theca with elongate rows of radial plates. Unfortunately this form has not yet been found in Europe.

Orbitremites is similar to *Deltoblastus* with a sub-globular theca and comes from the **Lower Carboniferous** of England and Germany.

Orophocrinus, also from the **Lower Carboniferous** of England, has shorter ambulacra with a conical or club-shaped theca.

Deltoblastus

Orophocrinus

Orbitremites

Cystoids

Cystoids were a minor group of Palaeozoic echinoderms with a sub-spherical theca composed of large plates punctured by numerous respiratory pores. There is a ring of plates on top of the theca surrounding the mouth. There are usually a series of arms around the mouth, used for food collecting. The anus is on the side of the theca. Many cystoids had a short stem, but others cemented their theca to a firm substrate. Cystoids are found throughout northwest Europe as well as Spain and the Alps. **Pleurocystites** and **Lepocrinites** are typical cystoids from the **Lower Ordovician** to **Upper Devonian**.

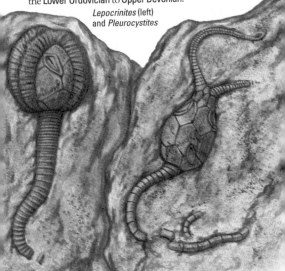

Lepocrinites (left)
and *Pleurocystites*

Crinoids

Crinoids, sometimes called sea lilies, although they are not plants, are mostly stalked echinoderms with a test or **theca** on a stem which is usually attached to the substrate. The skeleton is divided into two main regions. There is a lower **pelma**, comprising a **holdfast** which anchors the crinoid to the substrate and a stem that may be several metres long in some forms and can be covered by thin **cirri**, and a **crown** which includes the **calyx**, which is the main body. The calyx has a mouth and anus on its upper surface, the latter sometimes being extended to form an elongate **anal tube**. Surrounding the calyx is a food gathering apparatus comprising a series of arms with numerous branches or **pinnules** over their surface. At the base the arms are not separate, **fixed arms**, but become separate, the **free arms** as they fan up upwards. The stem is composed of numerous ossicles with a central hole or lumen. Fragments of stem and ossicles are a major constituent of crinoidal limestones. Although the stem may be several metres long it is usually less than 1 m long. A few forms are free swimming, with no stem. Some stemless forms have a holdfast which is used like legs to move across the sea bed. Some Jurassic forms lived attached to floating logs and had stems over 15 m long.

Crinoids are rare today, preferring to live in deeper waters than starfishes and sea urchins. In the Upper Palaeozoic and the Jurassic crinoids were a very important component of sea floor communities, and in the Cretaceous were an important part of the surface community in some seas.

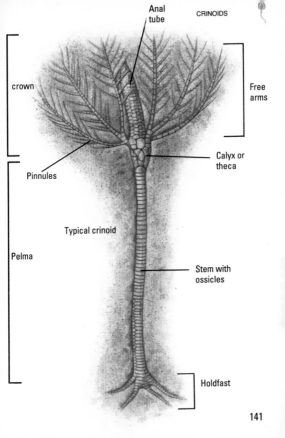

Anal tube

CRINOIDS

crown

Free arms

Pinnules

Calyx or theca

Typical crinoid

Pelma

Stem with ossicles

Holdfast

141

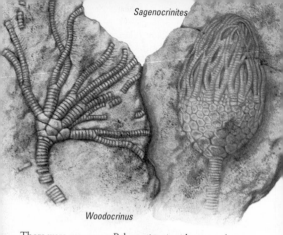

Sagenocrinites

Woodocrinus

There were very many Palaeozoic crinoid genera, the two illustrated here being fairly typical, relatively common forms. It should be noted that complete specimens are rare but isolated ossicles and thecal plates can occur in vast numbers.

Woodocrinus has a rather small cone shaped calyx with 20 robust branching arms. The stem has round ossicles. Common in the **Upper Carboniferous** of England.

Sagenocrinites has a large ovoid crown with conical calyx with numerous polygonal plates. The stem has round ossicles. Common in the **Silurian** of England and Sweden.

Pentacrinites has a relatively long stem, a small calyx and long arms with thin, elongate crowded cirri. The ossicles of the stem are star-shaped with five points and a petal-like pattern on the articulatory face. The pinnules are long, fine and very numerous. Complete specimens are rare. The characteristic star-shaped ossicles are very abundant in marine **Jurassic** rocks over most of Europe.

Star-shaped ossicle

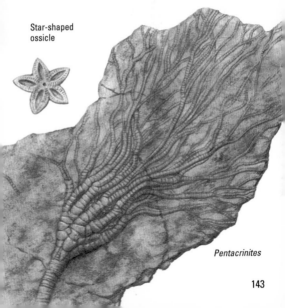

Pentacrinites

143

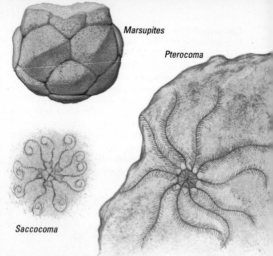

Marsupites

Pterocoma

Saccocoma

Saccocoma is a benthic crinoid with a small calyx and five arms which split into two and are usually coiled at the distal end. Common in the Solnhofen Limestone of Bavaria in mass mortality assemblages. Upper Jurassic to Lower Cretaceous.

Pterocoma is a free living crinoid with no stem. It has ten elongate, feather-like arms with long pinnules. Rare in Germany. Upper Jurassic to Cretaceous.

Marsupites is a free swimming crinoid with a large calyx. Isolated plates from the calyx are common in the chalk of northwest Europe, and are characterized by a pattern of V-shaped ridges. Upper Cretaceous.

Crinoidal limestone

The skeletons of dead crinoids usually break down into thousands of constituent parts. When crinoids are in great abundance these elements can be a major component of the sediment. Being easily winnowed by gentle currents, crinoid debris can accumulate in vast thicknesses in areas where water currents are slower, such as at the foot of large reefs. Some crinoid limestones contain larger fragments of crinoid stems which record the passage of large hurricanes over the seas where the crinoids lived, smashing them up while still alive. The illustration shows crinoidal limestone in its natural state and after cutting and polishing.

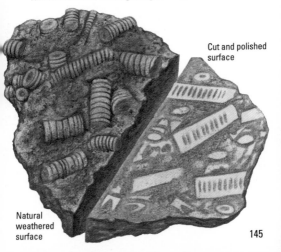

Cut and polished surface

Natural weathered surface

145

Brittle stars

Brittle stars or ophiuroids are common in Europe today. They have a very small **central disc** which contains the gut and other organs, and is surrounded by five snake-like long arms used for feeding and locomotion. Each arm is composed of small, highly modified plates, the **vertebrae**, which function to make the arms very flexible. The fossil record for brittle stars is extensive, going back to the Ordovician, although they are only locally common. They have changed little in overall shape and fossil forms are very similar to living brittle stars.

Lapworthura is a typical ophiuroid with a star-shaped, relatively large central disc and robust arms with conspicuous spines laterally. It is relatively common in the **Upper Ordovician** to **Silurian** of the UK.

Lapworthura

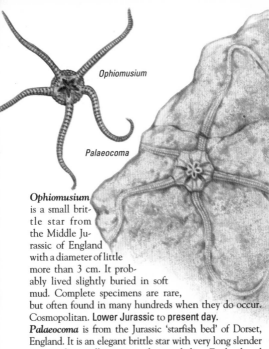

Ophiomusium

Palaeocoma

Ophiomusium
is a small brittle star from
the Middle Jurassic of England
with a diameter of little
more than 3 cm. It probably lived slightly buried in soft
mud. Complete specimens are rare,
but often found in many hundreds when they do occur.
Cosmopolitan. **Lower Jurassic to present day.**

Palaeocoma is from the Jurassic 'starfish bed' of Dorset,
England. It is an elegant brittle star with very long slender
arms and a small, pentagonal central disc. England and
Switzerland. **Lower Jurassic.** Isolated vertebrae from brittle
stars are very common as micro fossils showing that brittle
stars were often common, but rarely preserved complete.

147

Starfish

Starfish occur today in shallow and deep seas from the poles to the tropics. Rarely more than a few tens of centimetres across, they are characterized by having five or more thick arms. The lower surface is covered with tube feet, and a mouth is placed at the centre of the star on the underside.

Metopaster is a pentagonal starfish with very short arms each bordered by large plates, and with two apical triangular plates. The upper surface of this starfish is covered with a mosaic of numerous small plates. Isolated plates are common in the chalk over most of northern Europe. **Upper Cretaceous** to **present day**.

Metopaster

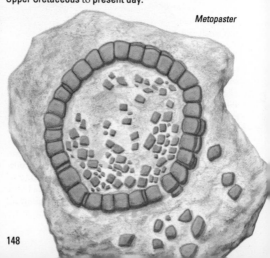

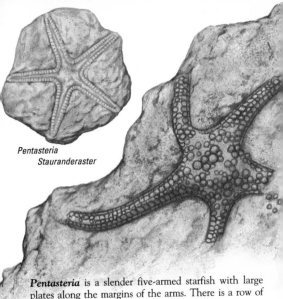

Pentasteria
Stauranderaster

Pentasteria is a slender five-armed starfish with large plates along the margins of the arms. There is a row of smaller plates between the marginal plates of each arm. Like most starfishes, complete specimens are rare. Cosmopolitan. Jurassic to Eocene.

Stauranderaster is similar to Pentasteria, with long, narrow, straight-sided arms fringed with large marginal plates. On the upper surface the marginal plates of each arm unite in the middle. Cosmopolitan. Upper Jurassic to Upper Cretaceous.

149

Sea urchins

Sea urchins or echinoids are common in all shallow seas today. They are world wide in distribution, but are more diverse in warm and tropical seas. They share in common a box-like test, composed of interlocking calcitic plates, and are usually covered with movable spines. There are many forms, with diverse ecologies. Some burrow deep within in the sediment and are usually covered with fine spines which are pressed close to the test. Others live on the sea floor or bore into rocks. Typically the test is circular or oval in outline and usually globular, but a number of forms are biscuit-like. A simplistic two-fold system can be used to classify urchins, although this does not reflect their true evolutionary relationships. **Regular urchins** are circular in outline and display an almost perfect five-fold symmetry. **Irregular urchins** are bilaterally symmetrical, but remnants of an original five-fold symmetry remain. The latter group are mostly burrowers.

At the top of the test in regular urchins there is a ring of plates, the **periproct**, with the anus. At the bottom is a ring of plates, the **peristome**, which surrounds a mouth with strong jaws called the **aristotles lantern**. There are notches to accommodate gills within the peristome. The main body of the test is divided into a series of paired plates called **ambulacra**, between which there are another row of paired plates, the **interambulacra**. Ambulacral plates have small pairs of holes, the **pore pairs**, through which the tube feet are operated. Interambulacral plates often possess articulatory bosses for spines.

In the irregular urchins the test is often highly modified. In some forms it is heart- or cone-shaped, and in some it may be tubular. A few even have large holes or **lunules,** which pass right through the test. In flat forms there may be a system of canals on the underside which channel water for feeding. In most irregular urchins the mouth has moved from a central position to a frontal position, while the anus has moved from the top of the test to a more posterior position. The ambulacra may be less distinct, but are always present. Sea Urchins have a fossil record ranging from the **Ordovician** to the **present day.**

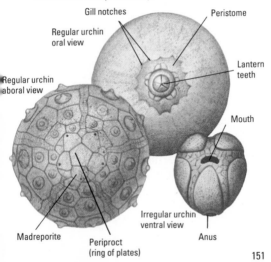

Gill notches

Peristome

Regular urchin oral view

Lantern teeth

Regular urchin aboral view

Mouth

Madreporite

Periproct (ring of plates)

Irregular urchin ventral view

Anus

151

Archaeocidaris is a regular echinoid with a sub-spherical test composed of large pentagonal plates on the interambulacra bearing conspicuous spine bosses. When complete the test is slightly flattened, but it is usually found with the plates disarticulated. It is rarely found with its spines intact. Cosmopolitan. **Lower Carboniferous** to **Permian**.

Hemicidaris is a small to medium, globular, slightly flattened regular echinoid with large spine bosses on the interambulacra. The large spine bosses are perforated and in offset pairs. The spines are often twice as long as the test is wide. Common in shallow water limestones throughout Europe. **Jurassic to Cretaceous.**

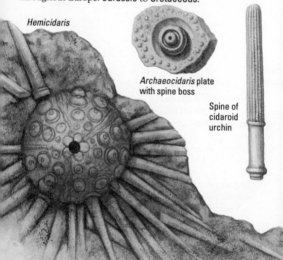

Hemicidaris

Archaeocidaris plate with spine boss

Spine of cidaroid urchin

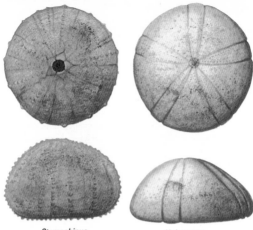

Stomechinus   *Holectypus*

Stomechinus is a small regular urchin with many small spine bosses on the interambulacra, and even smaller ones on the ambulacral plates. Test somewhat flattened with a circular outline. Cosmopolitan. Middle Jurassic to Cretaceous.

Holectypus is a flat dome-shaped irregular echinoid with circular outline covered with numerous small tubercles and has a very small circlet of plates at the top. The periproct is ringed with large gill notches, and there is a pear-shaped opening for the anus next to the mouth. The ambulacral plates are arranged in groups of three. Cosmopolitan. Jurassic to Cretaceous.

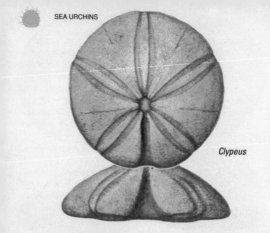

Clypeus

Pygaster

Nucleolites

Clypeus is a relatively large irregular urchin with a diameter commonly reaching 10 cm. It has a circular outline and is relatively flat. There is a large triangular pit posteriorly midway between two rows of ambulacral plates. Surface covered in small spine bosses. Cosmopolitan. Particularly common in the Cotswolds region of central England where locals stick three round pebbles on the underside and sell them as pixie stools. **Middle to Upper Jurassic.**

Nucleolites is a small to medium-sized irregular echinoid with a flat test with slightly square to oval outline. The surface is covered in minute spine bosses. Ambulacra petal-like. Periproct developed on upper surface as large groove on posterior margin. Cosmopolitan. **Middle to Upper Jurassic.**

Pygaster is a medium to large, slightly pentagonal irregular echinoid covered with numerous small tubercles. Lower surface flattened. The periproct is on the upper surface, just touching the apical disc producing a keyhole-shaped slot. Surface of test covered with small tubercles. Cosmopolitan. **Middle Jurassic to Upper Cretaceous.**

Micraster

Micraster
lateral view

Disaster

Holaster

Holaster
lateral view

Conulus

Echinocorys

Disaster is a small irregular echinoid which is usually less than 3 cm long. The test is truncated and somewhat square when viewed posteriorly. Surface covered with very small tubercles. This echinoid is relatively common in calcareous mudstones of England and northern France. **Middle Jurassic** to **Lower Cretaceous**.

Holaster is an irregular echinoid with rounded test with small indentation posteriorly where an ambulacrum meets the edge of the test. On top the ambulacra resemble fine petals, but they rapidly broaden and become fainter. The posterior margin is flattened. Cosmopolitan. **Lower Cretaceous** to **Eocene**.

Echinocorys is a dome-like irregular echinoid with an oval outline when viewed from above. Common in the chalk over most of Europe. **Upper Cretaceous** to **Palaeocene**.

Micraster is a distinctive heart-shaped echinoid common in the chalk of northern Europe. Like *Holaster* it has fine, petal-like ambulacra on its upper most surface. The anus is on a flat posterior surface. The mouth is hidden on the lower surface by a small projection of the test. Cosmopolitan. **Upper Cretaceous** to **Palaeocene**.

Conulus is a conical to high acute dome-shaped irregular echinoid with a centrally placed mouth on a flat lower surface. Circular to slightly oval outline from above. Common in the chalk over much of northwest Europe. **Cretaceous**.

Clypeaster is a spectacular, large, pentagonal, somewhat pyramid-like irregular echinoid with prominent lobe-shaped ambulacra. The bottom surface is flat with a depression in the centre where the mouth lies. Both surfaces are entirely covered with small tubercles. Five grooves radiate from the centre of the upper surface through the middle of the ambulacra. Internally there are a number of struts which support the test. Cosmopolitan. Eocene to present day.

Amphiope or the biscuit urchin is an irregular echinoid which is very flat with two prominent holes which perforate the test in the posterior portion. The ambulacra are petal-like but do not extend to the margin of the test. Surface covered in small tubercles. Cosmopolitan. Oligocene to Miocene. Many closely related forms survive to the present day.

Hagenowia is one of the most bizarre of all echinoids. It is a burrowing form which has a small, cylindrical test extended anteriorly into an elongate rostrum. One of the ambulacra extends for the full length of the rostrum. Cosmopolitan, but not common. Upper Cretaceous.

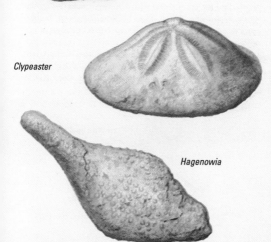

Amphiope

Clypeaster

Hagenowia

GRAPTOLITES

Graptolites are an extinct group of small colonial organisms related to marine, filter feeding hemichordates which today inhabit cryptic environments in most seas. Graptolites were mainly free-living planktonic organisms which occurred in vast numbers during the Lower Palaeozoic. They underwent rapid evolutionary change, occur world wide and as such are very important zone fossils. The part of the graptolite usually found as a fossil consists of an organic walled skeleton comprising a series of cups or **thecae** arranged along a rod-like structure, into the **stipe**. The first theca is called the **sicula**, and is a conical cup with a pointed **nema** or **virgula** at its apex. The thecae may be simple cups or highly elaborate structures with complex **apertural openings** often with **apertural spines**. A spine at the aperture of the sicula is known as the **virgella**. The graptolite animal is referred to as a zooid, and it may have had a small headshield which projected from the theca. There would also have been a filter apparatus used for feeding.

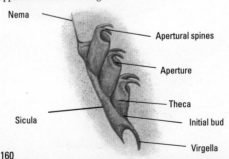

Nema

Apertural spines

Aperture

Theca

Sicula

Initial bud

Virgella

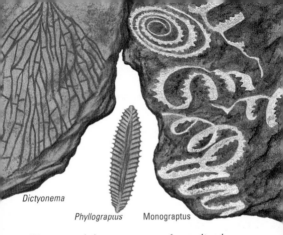

Dictyonema

Phyllograptus   Monograptus

Dictyonema belongs to a group of graptolites known as dendroids. They all have multiple branching stipes which are connected by small cross-bars. The theca are small and inconspicuous. Dendroid graptolites range from the Cambrian to Lower Permian.

Phyllograptus is shaped like a thin leaf. It comprises four stipes which sit back to back. Theca are united with adjacent theca for much of their length, giving a broad aspect to the stipe. Cosmopolitan. Ordovician.

Monograptus is a general name given to a group of graptolites in which there is only a single stipe. The shape of the theca is highly variable within the group. There are many types of Monograptus, some are spiral, others are straight. Cosmopolitan. Silurian to Middle Devonian.

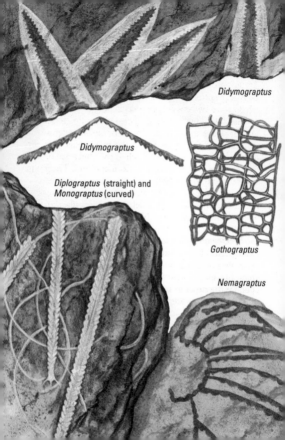

Didymograptus

Didymograptus

Diplograptus (straight) and
Monograptus (curved)

Gothograptus

Nemagraptus

Nemagraptus is a graptolite with branches at regular intervals. These branches become new stipes, each bearing thecae. The two initial stipes are elegantly curved with thecae on the inside edge. Cosmopolitan. Upper Ordovician.

Didymograptus is a general name given to graptolites which have two stipes separated from each other except at the sicula. They are often shaped like tuning forks, and may have the theca on the inside or outside edge of the stipes. When the theca are on the inside edge they are termed pendent or declined; when the theca are on the outside edge they are reclined. Cosmopolitan. The group is restricted to the Ordovician.

Gothograptus belongs to a group of graptolites known as retiolitids. They have a very delicate, basket-like skeleton which was very light, possibly as an aid to floating. Cosmopolitan. The retiolitid group of graptolites ranges from the Ordovician to Silurian.

Diplograptus has two stipes lying back to back, with theca projecting outwards, a condition called scandent. Some graptolite species may begin in this condition, but then open up the stipes in later life of the colony. Cosmopolitan. Ordovician to Silurian.

Monograptus is a monograptid very different from that illustrated on p. 161. This graptolite has very long, thin stipes which form a very open helical spiral or mat. At first glance these graptolites resemble scribble-like pencil marks on the rock. Cosmopolitan. Silurian.

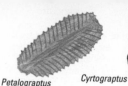

Petalograptus   **Cyrtograptus**

Petalograptus is a didymograptid with thecae of
varying sizes, beginning small, becoming larger and then
small again toward the tip, giving the colony a leaf-like
shape. Cosmopolitan. **Silurian.**

Cyrtograptus is a monograptid similar to *Nemagraptus* in
general form. The first stipe is elegantly spiral, with sec-
ondary stipes at regular intervals. **Silurian.**

Distorted graptolites

Distorted graptolites. Graptolite skeletons contain only organic material, most probably the
protein collagen. Thus most graptolites tend to
be squashed flat. In the north and west of the UK
and in Scandinavia, many rocks containing graptolites have been deformed during continental
collisions and has resulted in the deformation of the fossils. This is
particularly marked in the distortion of graptolites.

FOSSIL VERTEBRATES

Vertebrates possess an internal, multi-component skeleton composed of calcium phosphate. It takes the form of bone, and enamel and dentine in teeth. In most cases it is hard, chemically inert, and preserves very well as fossils. Despite this, vertebrate remains are not usually as abundant as those of invertebrates, partly because vertebrates are often rarer in life than invertebrates, and because many vertebrates produce less young than invertebrates, so that the quantity of vertebrate material available for the fossil record is generally less than for invertebrates.

Complete skeletons of vertebrates are rare, but isolated elements, especially teeth, can be very common. Under some circumstances teeth and bones may be concentrated due to high winnowing or predator activity. Such concentrations are known as bone beds. Several bone beds in Europe have become famous as sources of vertebrate material. At Aust cliff on the banks of the river Severn in England a Triassic bone bed yields remains of fish and reptiles in profusion, along with numerous coprolites, which represent fossil excreta. Similar bone beds occur in the Triassic of southern Germany.

Collecting fossil vertebrate remains may require more patience and time in the field than collecting fossil invertebrates. In the laboratory, vertebrate remains can often be extracted from limestone by the use of dilute organic acids such as acetic and formic acids at concentrations of 10%. These acids will dissolve limestone, but do not usually dissolve bone.

The earliest vertebrates – FISHES

The earliest vertebrate remains are small scale-like structures called **thelodonts** from the late Cambrian; they are probably from a fish-like animal without jaws which fed on detritus. More complete remains come from the Ordovician of South America and are considered to represent a primitive group of fishes called **agnathans**. Vertebrates only became common as fossils in the late Silurian, and by Devonian times many different groups of fishes had appeared. During this time vertebrates became adapted to terrestrial conditions, and by the end of the Devonian tetrapods (four-limbed vertebrates) had appeared.

Thelodont x 20

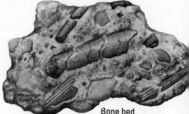

Bone bed

Jawless fishes

The living lampreys and hagfishes belong to the agnathans, and although these extant forms possess no readily preservable hard parts, their Palaeozoic relatives were often clad in hard protective bony plates and thelodonts. Most had a fish-shaped body, with a well-defined head covered with bony shields. Mainly freshwater, most had become extinct by the end of the Devonian.

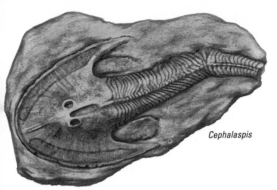

Cephalaspis

Cephalaspis is an agnathan with a fish-like body. The head is horseshoe-shaped and covered with bony shields. The head shield has two posterior-pointing spines laterally. The front of the headshield is rounded with the mouth underneath. There are two eyes high up on the headshield medially. The sides of the head shield have two elongate openings covered with many small plates. These areas are interpreted as sensory openings. There is a large pair of pectoral fins but no pelvic fins. A small dorsal fin is situated toward the tail. The body is clad in elongate, overlapping plates and the tail only slightly forked, with a large upper lobe with a fin on its lower surface. Common in some parts of northwest Europe. **Lower Devonian.**

Sharks and rays

Sharks have largely cartilaginous skeletons which do not preserve well. However most sharks have teeth which they shed continuously through life and which are resistant to erosion and preserve easily. Some sharks have spines which also preserve readily, and most have a covering of thousands of tooth-like scales or dermal denticles which resemble microscopic teeth. Thus sharks contribute a large number of skeletal remains to the fossil record, and as such isolated remains are common. Mineralized cartilage does not often preserve well, and as a consequence shark vertebrae and jaws tend to be rare as fossils.

Most sharks are marine but a few forms regularly enter freshwater, and some rays live permanently in rivers such as the Amazon. They have a range of diets and this is reflected in the great diversity of different tooth shapes. Although the large predatory sharks are perhaps the best known, both large and small sharks feed on invertebrates and have dentitions modified for crushing shells. The largest of all sharks, the basking and whale sharks, have small teeth and feed on plankton.

Variation in shark tooth morphology

Galeocerdo tooth, for cutting

Hybodus tooth, for tearing

Acrodus tooth, for crushing invertebra[t]

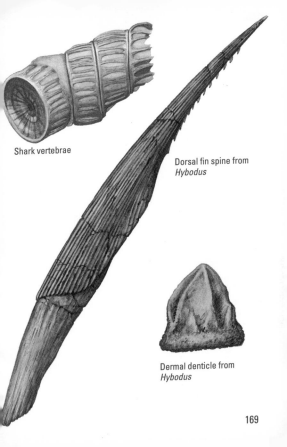

Shark vertebrae

Dorsal fin spine from *Hybodus*

Dermal denticle from *Hybodus*

169

Asteracanthus is a large hybodont shark, perhaps growing to over 4 m, with a dentition modified for crushing hard-shelled invertebrates. The teeth are elongate, platform-like elements with a strong median ridge, and ornament of finer radiating ridges. *Asteracanthus* has dorsal fin spines in front of the two dorsal fins, covered laterally with stellate tubercles. Males had barbed hook-like cephalic spines which were used in mating. Common in marine sediments in England, France and Germany. **Middle** and **Upper Jurassic.**

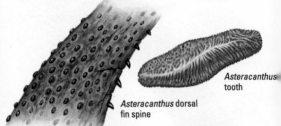

Asteracanthus tooth

Asteracanthus dorsal fin spine

Notidanus is a cow shark related to the modern six gill shark *Hexanchus*. Often only found as isolated teeth which are laterally compressed with a main cusp anteriorly followed by several cusps of decreasing size. There may be a serrated anterior margin to the first cusp with a row of mesial cusplets. Cosmopolitan. **Jurassic** to **present day** for this type of tooth.

Ptychodus is characterized by a dentition of square, dome-like teeth with an ornament of enamel ridges. Isolated teeth occur frequently in the chalk of northern Europe, and may reach a width of over 5 cm. Cosmopolitan. **Upper Cretaceous.**

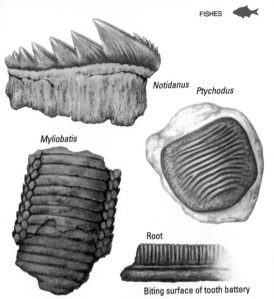

Notidanus

Ptychodus

Myliobatis

Root

Biting surface of tooth battery

Myliobatis is the Eagle Ray of modern seas, and has a good dental fossil record. The teeth form a platform which makes a large crushing surface. The upper surface is usually smooth from wear, but the root has a distinctive pattern of grooves and ridges. Individual teeth can clearly be defined, and occur in seven rows. There is a median row of wide teeth with three rows of smaller, polygonal teeth on either side. Cosmopolitan. **Eocene** to **present day**.

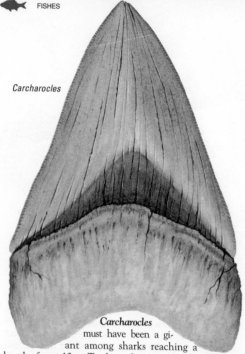

Carcharocles

Carcharocles

must have been a giant among sharks reaching a length of over 10 m. Teeth can be up to 20 cm high. They are triangular with a slightly forked root, laterally compressed crown with a fine serrated margin. *Carcharocles* probably fed on seals. Southern Europe. **Eocene** to Pliocene.

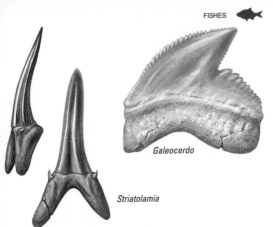

Galeocerdo

Striatolamia

Striatolamia is a name given to elongate, recurved, slender teeth from a fossil sand shark. The crown is high, with small lateral cusplets on a forked root and faint striations on the enamel. These and similar teeth are commonly found among the beach gravel in front of clay cliffs. Good places to hunt for them in southern England are the Isle of Sheppey in Kent and Barton on Sea in Hampshire. **Palaeocene** to **Oligocene**.

Galeocerdo is a shark whose teeth are laterally compressed with a backward pointing median cusp and anterior and posterior cusplets. The boundary between the crown and the root is strongly arched. Cosmopolitan. **Eocene** to **present day**.

Bony fishes or osteichthyans

Unlike the sharks and agnathans, most other fishes possess a bone skeleton and are called **osteichthyans** or bony fishes. They include the lungfishes, the sturgeons and the coelacanths as well as most of the familiar fish of today's rivers and seas such as salmon and perch. The earliest fossil remains are isolated scales from the late Silurian, but complete specimens are common from the early Devonian to the present day.

Lungfishes and allies

Lungfishes are living fossils. Only three species are alive today in Africa, South America and Australia, but formerly this group was more widespread, and were abundant in Europe from the Devonian to the Triassic. After Triassic times lungfishes appear to have been restricted to the southern hemisphere. It was from close relatives of the lungfishes that the tetrapods evolved in the Devonian.

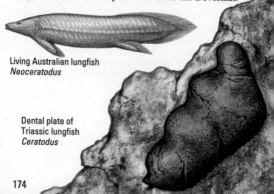

Living Australian lungfish
Neoceratodus

Dental plate of
Triassic lungfish
Ceratodus

174

Ceratodus is a common lungfish in the Triassic of Europe, but usually only its robust dental plates are found. These are crenulated platforms modified for crushing shelled invertebrates. Germany and England. **Triassic.**

Osteolepis is a very early bony fish with lobed fins and hard, enamel-coated diamond-shaped scales. The fins were lobed, with each lobe having a limb-like skeleton within. **Osteolepiforms** are one of a number of fish groups close to the ancestry of amphibians. Common in north-east Scotland and the Orkney Isles. **Devonian.**

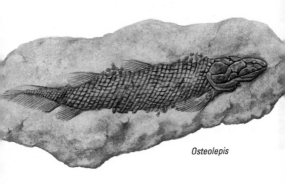

Osteolepis

Early ray-finned fishes or actinopterygia

These are fishes characterized by having bony rays in their fins. They first appeared in the Devonian, and are the most diverse group of fishes today. Early forms had hard enamel-coated scales, and the eyes were placed in a forward position on the skull.

Palaeoniscum

Palaeoniscum is a small fish with smooth, shiny, enamel-coated scales, a forked caudal fin and very prominent, anteriorly placed eyes. Cosmopolitan. **Carboniferous** to **Permian**.

Saurichthys is another fish with hard, shiny enamel scales. This ferocious fish is elongate, with long slender jaws armed with sharp, strongly ribbed teeth. England, Germany, Switzerland and Italy. **Triassic**.

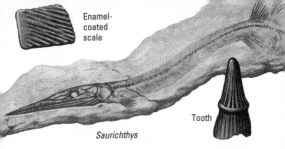

Enamel-coated scale

Tooth

Saurichthys

Dapedium is a deep-bodied, laterally compressed fish with rectangular or diamond-shaped scales, usually very shiny and dark brown or black when found in organic rich clays and shales. The head is covered with thick bony plates most of which possess enamel tubercles. The teeth are stylus-like. England, France and Germany. **Lower Jurassic.**

Dapedium

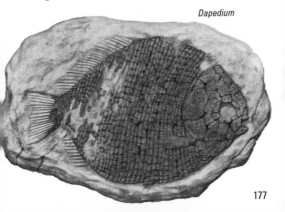

Lepidotes is a deep-bodied fish, but more fusiform than *Dapedium*. The body is covered with diamond-shaped enamelled scales. The tail is deeply forked. Teeth subspherical or stylus-like. Cosmopolitan. **Lower Jurassic to Lower Cretaceous.**

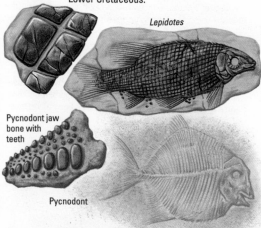

Lepidotes

Pycnodont jaw bone with teeth

Pycnodont

Pycnodonts are deep-bodied fish with dome-shaped teeth. They have a characteristic triangular bone in the roof of the mouth with several rows of teeth. The caudal fin is deeply forked and the dorsal and anal fins are long. The pelvic fins are situated underneath the pectoral fins. Cosmopolitan. **Jurassic to Eocene.**

Later ray-finned fishes

Leedsichthys was a filter feeding fish of gigantic proportions. It may have reached a length of over 10 m. The caudal fin was deeply forked with a span of 3 m. The most common remains of this fish are gill rakers: comb-like bones up to 6 cm in length with fine teeth which may have been periodically shed. Known from England and France. **Middle** and **Upper Jurassic**.

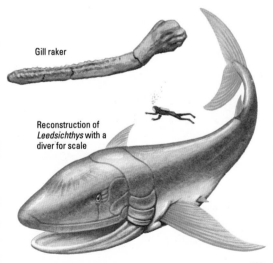

Gill raker

Reconstruction of *Leedsichthys* with a diver for scale

FISHES

There were a number of slender, elongate, predatory fish in the Mesozoic seas.

Aspidorhynchus has an elongate upper jaw, but only a very short lower jaw. It is found as beautiful complete specimens in the Solnhofen Limestone of Bavaria, but is also well known from England and France.

Belonostomus has both the upper and lower jaws elongated and occurs widely in Europe. Both range from the Jurassic to Cretaceous.

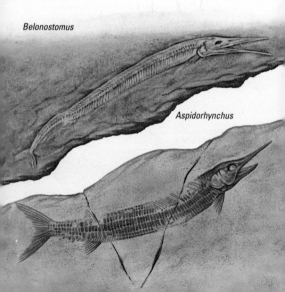

Belonostomus

Aspidorhynchus

Teleosts

The vast majority of living fishes belong to a group known as teleosts. This group includes the catfishes, carp and perches or acanthopterygians. Acanthopterygians are abundant as fossils from the Eocene to present day in Europe. They are characterized by dorsal fins with strong bony fin rays anteriorly.

Amphiperca is from the **Eocene** of Germany, but many other genera are found throughout Europe. In north Italy an Eocene site at Monte Bolca has become famous for the great beauty and diversity of its fossils, many of which are acanthopterygians.

Amphiperca

Mass mortality

Fish are sensitive to small changes in water chemistry, which can often result in mass deaths of thousands of individuals. The fossil record shows that this has been a common phenomenon in the past. Mass mortality assemblages are known where many thousands of individuals completely cover bedding plane surfaces. It is almost impossible to determine the cause of the mass mortality, but it is probably related to changes in salinity, temperature or a lack of oxygen in the water.

Mass mortality assemblage of small herrings

AMPHIBIANS

Amphibians are well known as fossils, especially in the Palaeozoic and early Mesozoic where they were often of very large size. Today amphibians are rather small but nonetheless diverse. The amphibian record is poor in the Jurassic and Cretaceous, but excellent specimens are known from the Tertiary, especially in Germany and France. During the Upper Palaeozoic amphibians were the dominant animals in the coal swamps of Europe and North America, but were gradually replaced by reptiles in the Permian. Large amphibians remained however, and were still important in the Triassic.

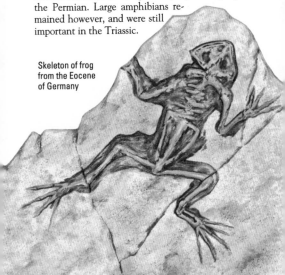

Skeleton of frog from the Eocene of Germany

REPTILES

Reptiles are a large group of extremely diverse tetrapods which are distinguished from amphibians by, amongst other things, the ability to reproduce without having to return to water for egg laying. This is because reptiles evolved an egg with a water-tight skin that prevents them from drying out. The earliest reptiles appeared in the Carboniferous and rapidly diversified into many highly distinct forms. The ancestry of the dominant tetrapods of today, the birds and mammals, can be traced back to various reptile groups through an excellent fossil record.

During the Mesozoic reptiles dominated both terrestrial and marine environments. Several groups of land dwelling reptiles returned to the seas and established an aquatic existence. The pterosaurs dominated the skies, while dinosaurs of various types dominated the land.

Terrestrial reptiles are not common as fossils in Europe, partly due to poor exposure of the right types of rocks. Most dinosaur-bearing strata in Europe is covered by rich agricultural land. In North America and central Asia where there are vast areas of desert the remains of reptiles are often common. However, Europe has good exposures of marine rocks, and consequently marine reptiles such as plesiosaurs and ichthyosaurs are extremely well known and relatively common.

Reptiles are classified on the basis of skull shape, with particular emphasis placed on the position of openings on the side of the skull known as **temporal fenestrae**. In one group, the **anaspids**, the skull has no opening. This group includes the familiar turtles. In the **euryapsids** there is an

184

opening in which two bones, the **squamosal** and the **post orbital** join underneath the opening. The plesiosaurs belong to this group. The **synapsid** skull also has only a single opening, but here the squamosal and post orbital bones join above the opening. This group includes the pelycosaurs such as the sail-backed reptile *Dimetrodon*, and is the condition found in the skulls of mammals. The **diapsid** skull has two openings with squamosal and post orbital bones united between the two holes. This is the condition found in crocodiles, dinosaurs and pterosaurs.

SKULL MORPHOLOGY

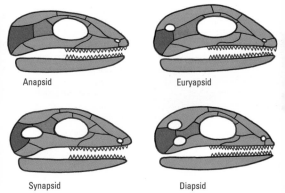

Anapsid

Euryapsid

Synapsid

Diapsid

Marine reptiles

During the Mesozoic a number of different reptile groups became adapted to varying degrees for living entirely in water, perhaps returning to the shore only to lay eggs. Plesiosaurs, crocodiles and turtles all appeared early in the Mesozoic. The most highly adapted to an aquatic existence were the ichthyosaurs: reptiles that superficially resemble dolphins and sharks in general body plan. Ichthyosaurs had an elongate skull, with very large eyes. The vertebrae of ichthyosaurs are concave on both anterior and posterior faces of the centrum, which makes them very easy to identify. The limbs of ichthyosaurs were modified into paddles, the front pair usually being considerably larger than the back. Most ichthyosaurs had small numerous teeth in very long jaws, although a few rare forms had back teeth modified for crunching. Ichthyosaurs gave birth to live young, and are presumed not to have returned to the shore at all.

All were fully marine, their remains commonly found in clays and shales where ammonites and belemnites are abundant.

Mixosaurus skeleton

Mixosaurus
was one of the earliest ichthyosaurs from the **Triassic** of Switzerland and Italy. It had a rather elongate body and only slightly forked caudal fin.

Ichthyosaurus was a common ichthyosaur in the Lower Jurassic of southern England, and was one of the first well-studied prehistoric reptiles. The large eye socket has a ring of bony plates which supported a very large eye. This suggests that ichthyosaurs had good eye sight perhaps for pursuing fast swimming prey. England, France and Germany. **Lower Jurassic.**

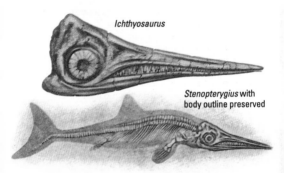

Ichthyosaurus

Stenopterygius with body outline preserved

Stenopterygius is known from many hundreds of individuals, some of which have their soft tissue outlines preserved as carbonized films. A few specimens are known with their stomachs full of hooklets from squids, and some have embryos preserved in the body cavity. Germany and England. **Lower Jurassic.**

Placodonts were a group of marine reptiles with a highly distinctive dentition of rounded or polygonal teeth. They fed on molluscs which they crushed with their robust dental battery. The limbs, although modified for locomotion underwater, were probably able to support them on land for short periods. **Placodus** was abundant in southern Europe. Isolated teeth are common in the marine **Triassic** of the Alpine region.

Teeth modified for crushing molluscs

Placodus reconstruction

Nothosaurus skeleton from the famous fossil beds of Ticino, Switzerland

Nothosaurs were small to medium-sized aquatic reptiles, partly adapted to an aquatic existence. They had elongate paddle-like limbs and a small head. The body was elongate. It is now thought that nothosaurs gave rise to pliosaurs (see p. 189).
Nothosaurus is common in the Triassic of Austria, Germany, Italy and Switzerland, but only isolated bones have been found in the UK.

Plesiosaurs were marine carnivores which dominated the seas during the Jurassic and early Cretaceous. They can be divided into two types for simplicity. Long-necked, small-skulled, graceful forms which fed largely on squids and fishes, and include the elasmosaurs; and gigantic, short-necked forms with massive skulls called pliosaurs, which fed on larger prey. Both Types were common in the Jurassic seas of England, France and Germany and are also known from Poland and Russia. Elasmosaur teeth are slender, gently recurved and have faint striations, whereas pliosaur teeth are large, strongly ribbed, with a round cross-section in Middle Jurassic forms, but triangular in later forms.

The main body of the vertebrae in plesiosaurs has two flat faces and the neural arch is fused to its upper surface in adults.

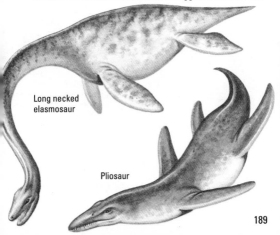

Long necked elasmosaur

Pliosaur

The teeth of plesioaurs are highly distinctive. The long-necked plesiosaurs had slender, elongate teeth with fine striations on the enamel surface. Pliosaurs had massive, sharp teeth with roots that sat deep within the jaws. Pliosaur teeth often had strong carinae on the surface, and some late Jurassic forms had two sharp keels.

Tooth of pliosaur
x 0.3

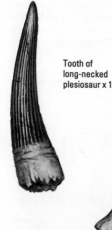

Tooth of
long-necked
plesiosaur x 1

Massive
root

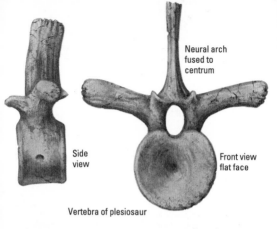

Neural arch
fused to
centrum

Side
view

Front view
flat face

Vertebra of plesiosaur

Front view
dished face

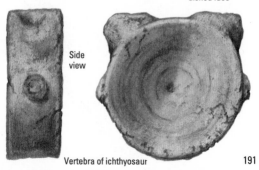

Side
view

Vertebra of ichthyosaur

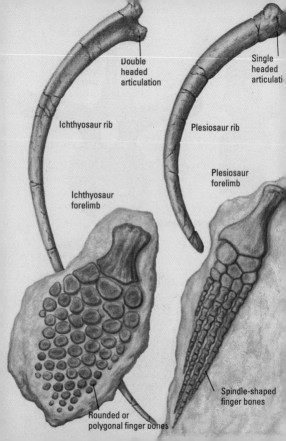

Double headed articulation

Single headed articulati[on]

Ichthyosaur rib

Plesiosaur rib

Ichthyosaur forelimb

Plesiosaur forelimb

Rounded or polygonal finger bones

Spindle-shaped finger bones

Crocodiles

Crocodiles are common in the fossil record from the Jurassic to the present. Both fully marine and semi-aquatic forms are known.

Steneosaurus is a fully marine crocodile with a dorsal armour of bony scutes with circular depressions. Snout highly elongated with numerous fine, pointed teeth. The limbs are reduced to paddles, with the forelimbs being much smaller than the rear limbs. England, France, Germany. There is a closely related form, *Teleosaurus*, which is slightly smaller. Jurassic.

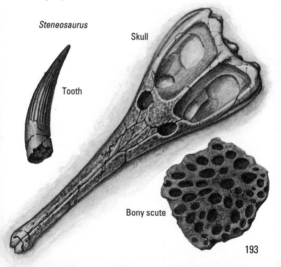

Steneosaurus

Tooth

Skull

Bony scute

193

Turtles

Turtles are relatively common fossils from the Cretaceous to the present, although they are first found in the Triassic. The turtle shell or **carapace** usually breaks up after death, so isolated pieces are more commonly found than entire skeletons. The carapace breaks up into thick bony plates with a smooth internal surface and an outer surface with flat-topped blisters, faint ridges or dimples. The edge of the plates has a crenulated suture. Widespread in both marine and non-marine sediments over all of Europe. *Trionyx* is a common turtle from the **Cretaceous** and **Tertiary** of Europe.

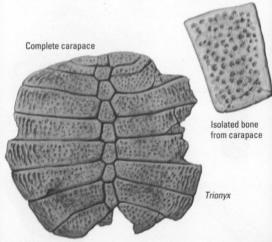

Complete carapace

Isolated bone from carapace

Trionyx

Pterosaurs

Pterosaurs were flying reptiles in which the fourth finger was excessively elongate, and supported a flight membrane extending from the body. Most pterosaurs were probably fish feeders. They range from the size of a sparrow to animals with wing spans of several metres; late Cretaceous pterosaurs were the largest ever flying animals. Pterosaurs are very rare fossils as their bones are extremely fragile, but excellent specimens have been collected from the Solnhofen Limestone of Bavaria. Pterosaurs range from the **Triassic** to **Cretaceous**.

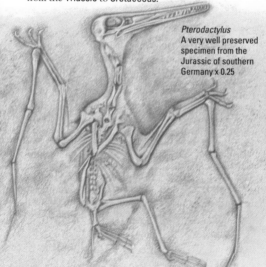

Pterodactylus
A very well preserved specimen from the Jurassic of southern Germany x 0.25

Dinosaurs

Dinosaurs are one of the most spectacular groups of land animals ever to have lived. They appeared in the Triassic evolving from crocodile-like ancestors and diversifying rapidly to become the dominant land animals for a period of more than 150 million years. They varied in size from small pigeon-sized forms to giants well over 20 m long. Some forms were insectivores, some giant flesh-eaters while others specialized on a wide variety of plant diets. By Cretaceous times dinosaurs had spread to every continent and were able to tolerate a range of climatic conditions including snowy winters.

Two main groups based on the structure of the hip bones are recognizable. The **Ornithischia** (bird-hipped) are dinosaurs in which the hip bone arrangement resembles that of birds, and includes familiar dinosaurs like *Iguanodon*, *Stegosaurus* and *Ankylosaurus*. The **Saurischia** (lizard-hipped) includes the long-necked sauropod dinosaurs such as *Apatosaurus*, *Diplodocus* and *Brachiosaurus* as well as the carnivorous *Megalosaurus* and *Tyrannosaurus*. Besides these forms this group also gave rise to the birds, so in some respects the dinosaurs did not become extinct, rather, one highly specialized group diversified and colonized the entire globe.

The fossil record of dinosaurs is patchy. Excellent faunas are known from North America, Argentina, Mongolia and China. The earliest finds were made in England, but most were of incomplete specimens. In Europe dinosaurs are still being found in Portugal, England, France and Germany.

Ankylosaur

Hadrosaur

Tyrannosaur

Stegosaur

Sauropod

Dinosaur teeth are highly distinctive and easily assigned to the major groups of dinosaurs. Teeth of carnivorous dinosaurs are usually pointed, slightly recurved and laterally compressed. They usually have a finely serrated lateral keel as in the teeth of *Megalosaurus* from the Jurassic of England, France, Germany and Portugal. Teeth of the long-necked sauropods such as *Cetiosauriscus* are usually spatulate or cylindrical.

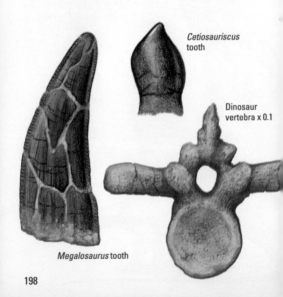

Cetiosauriscus tooth

Dinosaur vertebra x 0.1

Megalosaurus tooth

BIRDS

Because they have fragile skeletons, birds are extremely rare as fossils. The oldest undisputed bird fossils are of **Archaeopteryx** from the Upper Jurassic Solnhofen Limestone of Bavaria. This bird has feathers, but it also has teeth in the jaws and a long bony tail, and is more like a small dinosaur with some bird-like characteristics. It is known from only seven specimens, some of which are complete with impressions of the feathers preserved. The specimen illustrated here is in a museum in Berlin.

Archaeopteryx with impressions of feathers

MAMMALS

Mammals are the most familiar land animals today, and occupy many habitats. They range in size from rodents and insectivores 3-4 cm long to the marine leviathans such as the blue whale which may reach 30 m. Mammals are most easily characterized by the presence of hair (a feature only rarely preserved in the fossil record), that most give birth to live young and that all care for their young. Fossil mammals are most readily distinguished by having a single bone on each side of the lower jaw called the **dentary**, and having complex and varied teeth.

The mammal fossil record is good, and in Europe can be traced back to the Triassic. The origin of mammals goes back to the Mesozoic and perhaps even to the late Permian. The transition from synapsid reptile to mammal involved a complex series of evolutionary changes which resulted in the development of a jaw composed of a single bone and an ear with a delicate arrangement of bones used to transmit sound. At some point hair was acquired with a gradual loss of typical reptilian scales in all but a few mammal groups. During the Mesozoic mammals were small, perhaps a little bigger than domestic cats, but their remains are abundant in some places, suggesting they were quite common. After the end of the Cretaceous mammals diversified in what appears to have been a sudden burst of evolution. Within ten million years all the modern mammal orders had appeared. Mammals occupy all continents, including Antarctica, and have colonized all the oceans. A few are active flyers. Fossil mammals are common in the Tertiary non-marine basins of North America, Africa and South America. In Europe there are many sites which yield fossil mammals, some with exceptional quality of preservation. The rarest of all fossil mammal remains are those of man.

Mesozoic mammals

Large numbers of mammalian remains have been found in rocks in southern England and Wales, where deep fissures in Carboniferous limestone have been filled with Triassic and Jurassic muds. The remains are mostly fragmentary, but provide important evidence on the evolution of early mammals. They had elongate faces and were probably insectivores.

Bolodon from the **Upper Jurassic** of southern England had serrated, platform-like teeth with faint ridges, that measure only 2-3 mm high.

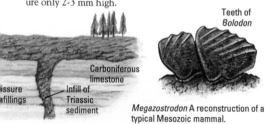

Teeth of *Bolodon*

Carboniferous limestone

Fissure fillings

Infill of Triassic sediment

Megazostrodon A reconstruction of a typical Mesozoic mammal.

Early tertiary mammals

The early Tertiary was a time of rapid diversification of the Mammalia, partly in response to gradual climatic changes, including a cooling of the climate in high latitudes and a reduction in the amount of forest through the Miocene. Members of most modern mammalian orders are found in the Lower Tertiary in Europe, including small early horses and tapirs, as well as carnivores and monkey-like mammals. Bats are particularly well known from the Eocene of Germany.

Microbunodon from the **Oligocene** of Germany was a rather pig-like animal with well-developed tusks and was related to modern hippos.

Microbunodon

Later tertiary mammals

By Miocene times large areas of Europe had become grass-land, and mammals adapted well to the new habitats. Their remains are common, especially the grinding teeth of herbivores, but large cats and other carnivores are also found. *Dinotherium* was a large, elephant-like mammal, but with downward curving tusks in the lower jaw. The molar teeth were large and modified for chewing and grinding tough plant material. The biting surface of the molars is characteristic with enamel ridges, often showing wear marks. Cosmopolitan on mainland Europe. Miocene.

Machairodus is one of a number of sabre-toothed cats which were a common component of the European mammal fauna. Cosmopolitan. Upper Miocene to Lower Pliocene.

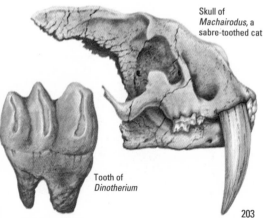

Skull of
Machairodus, a
sabre-toothed cat

Tooth of
Dinotherium

Mammals of the ice age

Approximately two million years ago Europe was subjected to a series of cooling events which resulted in an expansion of the polar ice caps, such that large areas were covered by an ice sheet, often up to several kilometres thick. Europe lay at the boundary between the glaciated and unglaciated realms. This change of climate had a dramatic effect on plant and animal life. Many of the Tertiary mammals became extinct, while some forms adapted to the new conditions in various ways. In Europe during the cold spells mammoths, woolly rhinoceros and musk ox became the dominant species, while during the interglacial periods lions, leopards, cave bears and hyenas thrived, along with a host of deer. Many of these forms also adapted to cold conditions. Elephants were an important component of the European Pleistocene mammalian fauna, with woolly mammoth, straight-tusked elephant and mastodons present at different times over most of Europe. But the most important colonizer of Europe during the late Pleistocene was a bipedal mammal approximately 1.5 m high with the ability to use tools, *Homo sapiens*.

Biting surface of molar tooth of woolly mammoth *Mammuthus*

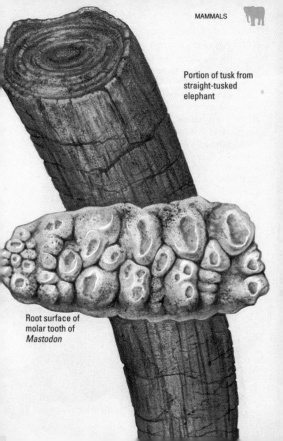

Portion of tusk from straight-tusked elephant

Root surface of molar tooth of *Mastodon*

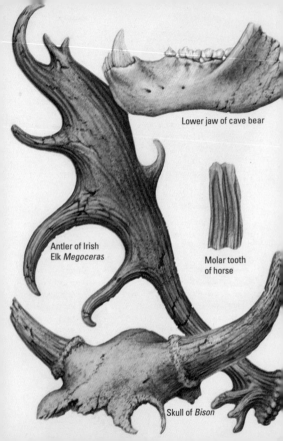

Lower jaw of cave bear

Antler of Irish
Elk *Megoceras*

Molar tooth
of horse

Skull of *Bison*

Megoceras giganteus, or Giant Irish Elk, had the largest antlers of any deer. The antlers have numerous points with the distal part of the antler flattened. Each antler may be up to 1.5 m long. This deer was widespread over most of northern Europe and many specimens have been recovered from peat deposits in Ireland. **Pleistocene** to just a few thousand years ago.

Bison and *Bos* are two large bovines, occurring in the Pleistocene of Europe. Skulls of both these animals are large with elongate, curved horn cores. Teeth are molariform for chewing. They are difficult to distinguish from each other. Common in **Pleistocene** of Britain, France and Germany through to Russia.

Equus caballus or Wild Horse was widespread over most of Europe during the Pleistocene. After the Ice Age it went into decline as a wild animal, but remained common in Europe due to domestication. Teeth occur frequently in **Pleistocene** river terrace gravels over most of Europe.

Ursus arctos or Cave Bear remains occur frequently in the Pleistocene. Their remains often accumulate with other bones in the bottoms of caves that were their dens. Regular collapsing of the caves and the formation of stalagmites frequently buried their skeletons along with broken and gnawed bones that were their prey. Found in limestone caves over most of Europe. **Pleistocene**.

FOSSIL PLANTS

Included in this section are the algae (including blue-green algae) and the diatoms as well as the more familiar groups of plants. Few plants have a mineralized skeleton, but despite this the fossil record of plants is good. Many plants produce woody tissues which are very easily preserved. Lignin (the material that wood is composed of) is very resistant to bacterial decay, and hence can remain buried long enough for mineralization to take place, or alternatively, degrade in place to a residue of coaly material. The record of fossil algae goes back into the Precambrian, but the terrestrial plants did not appear until the Silurian.

There have been episodes in the history of the Earth when plant remains have accumulated in such profusion as to produce huge deposits of coal. The most notable of these times in Europe and North America was during the Carboniferous. Elsewhere in the world such deposits accumulated in the Permian, Cretaceous and the Oligocene.

Excellent areas where large numbers of fossil plants can be collected occur throughout Europe. In the UK numerous plant localities have been discovered. On the Isle of Mull in Scotland plant beds occur trapped between volcanic lavas of Palaeocene age. Throughout the Carboniferous coal fields of the UK and Germany fossil plants occur above and below coal seams, often very well preserved. Early plants occur in Devonian sandstones in Wales, while Jurassic plants are abundant on the Yorkshire coast and Cretaceous plants occur in profusion near Hastings in Sussex.

Bacteria

Bacteria, also known as prokaryotes, are simple organisms that are usually single celled or grow in filaments or sheets of associated cells. They lack a cell nucleus and most of the organelles found in the cells of higher animals and plants. There are many different types distinguished mainly on bio-chemical grounds. Some types of photosynthetic bacteria have a good fossil record because their photosynthetic activity results in the precipitation of fine layers of limestone.

Stromatolites are finely laminated, dome or pillar-like structures composed of calcium carbonate formed by photosynthetic blue-green algae. Such structures range from small to several metres across and several metres high. They have been found in some of the world's oldest sedimentary rocks, and are amongst the earliest fossils known. Both freshwater and marine forms are known. **Early Precambrian to present day.**

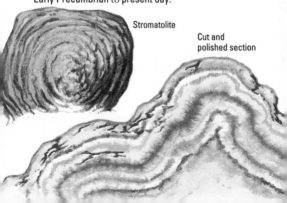

Stromatolite

Cut and polished section

Algae

Algae are simple plants that do not produce true leaves or stems. However, they can produce quite complex structures and may have elaborate shapes. Although mostly small, some forms such as kelp can reach gigantic, almost tree-like proportions. A few algae produce mineralized tubes or even structures with a superficial resemblance to coral, as a by-product of photosynthetic activity. Algal remains can be important binders of sediment in coral reef environments.

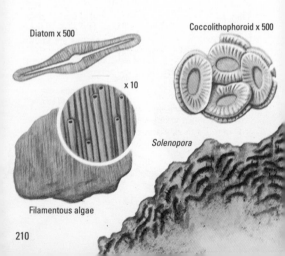

Diatom x 500

Coccolithophoroid x 500

x 10

Solenopora

Filamentous algae

Filamentous algae is a general term for the many types of algae that produce long filaments, which occasionally can be mineralized. One such algae is known to have flourished in a meteorite crater lake in southern Germany during the **Miocene**.

Diatoms are unicellular, microscopic plants that produce a silica skeleton which takes the form of a box with a lid, each part called a **frustule**. Diatoms live in both fresh and marine water, and accumulate in thick layers in some lakes to form the rock diatomite. They have a commercial use as fine abrasives and filters. Diatoms range from the **Mesozoic** to the **present day**.

Coccolithophoroids are unicellular, microscopic algae that produce a skeleton of calcitic shields, each composed of small overlapping plates. They can only be seen easily with the aid of a powerful electron microscope, but they are easy to collect as the **Cretaceous** chalks of northwest Europe are composed almost entirely of their remains. Arguably coccolithophoroids are the most common fossils in the world.

Solenopora is a tubular alga that produces dome-shaped colonies with numerous branching columns composed of distinct tiers. It is common in the Jurassic Portland Stone of Dorset, England, where blocks rich in *Solenopora* are used as an ornamental building stone. **Jurassic**.

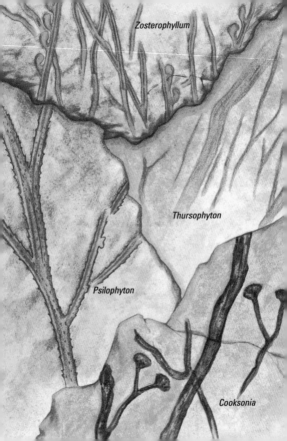

Early land plants

The first plants to appear on land were small and simple, consisting mainly of tubular stems, some with small leaf-like structures adjacent to the stem. Branching was usually simple splitting into two. Most produced terminal or laterally placed fruiting bodies (**sporangia**) which were spore-bearing.

Psilophyton has erect stems which repeatedly branch. Each stem is clad in small thorny leaves. Sporangia born laterally on branches. Wales. **Devonian.**

Thursophyton is an early plant that has erect stems clad with small scale-like leaves. Side branches are present at irregular intervals. There is some Y-shaped branching towards the top of the stems. **Devonian.**

Cooksonia is a small plant with bifurcating stems. There is usually an oval-shaped sporangium (spore capsule) at the end of the branches. Species are distinguished by the degree of branching and shape of the sporangia. Common in non-marine sediments in the Czech Republic, England, Germany, Wales and North America. **Silurian to Devonian.**

Zosterophyllum is an early plant with erect stems, with multiple branching close to ground level. The upper portions of the erect stems are clad with oval-shaped spore capsules on short stalks. Scotland. **Devonian.**

PLANTS

Club mosses

Properly known as **lycopods**, the club mosses may have their origins in the Silurian; a few forms are still extant. They reached their greatest diversity and abundance, however, in the Carboniferous. In size they range from small, ground-covering plants to giants over 30 m tall. They have distinctive stems and roots, with the stems covered with a spiral arrangement of diamond-shaped leaf scars, and roots clad with elongate, evenly spread branches or rootlets.

Carboniferous coal swamp

Different names are often given to the various parts of fossil plants, as they are often found separated. Thus in club mosses the stems may be referred to the genus **Lepidodendron** and roots referred to the genus **Stigmaria**. The fruiting bodies are called **Lepidostrobus**. These plants were very important in the formation of Carboniferous coal swamps.

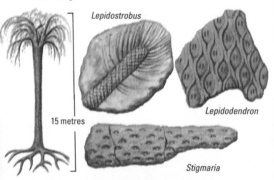

Lepidostrobus

Lepidodendron

15 metres

Stigmaria

Lepidodendron was a mighty, tree-sized club moss which may have reached over 30 m high. There are many species distinguished mainly by the shapes of the leaf scars on the stems, which are usually diamond-shaped with a series of ridges or a circular pit in the centre. It is very common in the **Upper Carboniferous** over most of Europe.

215

Ferns

Ferns are a diverse group of plants characterized by feathery or strap-like leaves or fronds, growing from a central body at ground level or on top of tall stems. Although an ancient group, ferns are still diverse today. They are common fossils and their origins can be traced to the Devonian.

Pecopteris was a tall tree fern up to 10 m high with elongate fronds up to 1 m long. **Carboniferous** to **Permian**.

Archaeopteris is possibly intermediate between fir trees and ferns. The leaves were oval to almost circular and overlapped each other. Cosmopolitan. **Devonian** to **Carboniferous**.

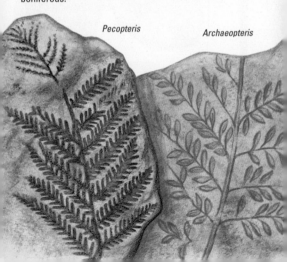

Pecopteris

Archaeopteris

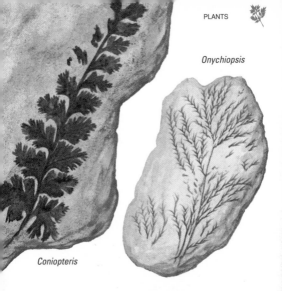

Onychiopsis

Coniopteris

Onychiopsis is a delicate fern with broad fronds of short, narrow leaves. Sussex, England, Germany and France. **Lower Cretaceous.**

Coniopteris is a common fern with long thin fronds with offset, incised, serrated leaves. England, especially the Yorkshire coast. **Jurassic.**

Seed ferns

The seed ferns, or pteridosperms, are so called because they had fern-like leaves and large pollen-bearing structures known as **potonea**. Most were tall, tree-like plants reaching heights of up to 8 m. Seeds of pteridosperms are sometimes referred to the genus *Trigonocarpus*. Individual leaves are called **pinnules** and each frond comprises many pinnules. They were abundant in the Carboniferous, and also in the Mesozoic where they formed an important component of the flora.

Telangium has delicate fern-like fronds with deeply divided pinnules with very fine veins. *Telangium* ranges from the Devonian to the Permian, but ferns similar in overall form to this are also common in the Mesozoic.

Alethopteris has narrow, elongate fronds in which the pinnules are united along the midrib without stems. Pinnules elongate with prominent central vein. UK. Carboniferous.

Neuropteris is a common tree fern with large fronds of delicate, oval to slightly elongate pinnules with a single elongate or sub-triangular terminal pinnule. UK. Carboniferous.

Mariopteris had large fronds with serrated leaflets. UK. Carboniferous to Permian.

Mariopteris

Neuropteris

Alethopteris

Telangium

Horsetails

The horsetails are a primitive group of plants that although not diverse today, are certainly abundant (and can be a pest) in many places in Europe. Most living species are small, never much more than a metre in height, but fossil forms were often gigantic. Stems of horsetails are characterized by being straight with well-spaced rings of leaf-scars. Between the leaf-scars the stem is vertically ribbed.

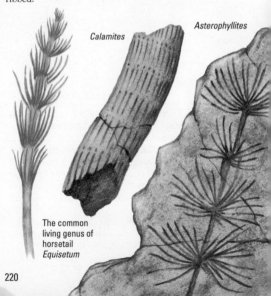

Calamites

Asterophyllites

The common living genus of horsetail *Equisetum*

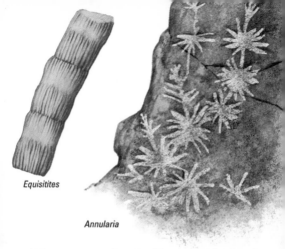

Equisitites

Annularia

Calamites is a common fossil horsetail with relatively long, broad stems. Cosmopolitan. **Carboniferous.**

Asterophyllites is not a true genus, but a term given to needle-like *Calamites* leaves. Cosmopolitan. **Carboniferous.**

Annularia, like *Asterophyllites*, is not a true genus, but a name applied to rings of *Calamites* leaves. The difference between these and *Asterophyllites* is the relative width of the leaves: they are slightly wider in *Annularia*. Cosmopolitan. **Carboniferous.**

Equisitites has a straight stem divided into discrete segments like all horsetails, each bounded by a ring of elongate leaves. Cosmopolitan. **Carboniferous** to **Cretaceous.**

Cycads and Bennetitales

This is not a natural grouping, but these plants are included together because they have a remarkable similarity of leaf and overall plant shape. There are many important structural differences that are only apparent with microscopic examination. Both groups, however, possess frond-like leaves with numerous elongate leaves or **pinnae**, along a thin central stem or **rachis**. Both also have a low, dome-like trunk with irregularly diamond-shaped leaf scars. Living cycads, or sago palms, are restricted to the southern hemisphere, are very slow growing and becoming rare in the wild. *Cycadeoidea* has a low, dome-shaped trunk with spiral pattern of diamond-shaped leaf scars. There may be branches of the main trunk. **Jurassic** to **Cretaceous**.

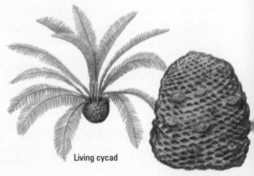

Living cycad

Trunk of *Cycadeoidea*

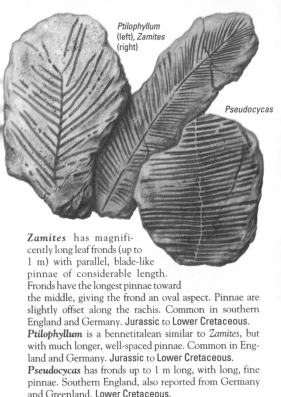

Ptilophyllum (left), *Zamites* (right)

Pseudocycas

Zamites has magnificently long leaf fronds (up to 1 m) with parallel, blade-like pinnae of considerable length. Fronds have the longest pinnae toward the middle, giving the frond an oval aspect. Pinnae are slightly offset along the rachis. Common in southern England and Germany. Jurassic to Lower Cretaceous.

Ptilophyllum is a bennetitalean similar to *Zamites*, but with much longer, well-spaced pinnae. Common in England and Germany. Jurassic to Lower Cretaceous.

Pseudocycas has fronds up to 1 m long, with long, fine pinnae. Southern England, also reported from Germany and Greenland. Lower Cretaceous.

Fir trees, conifers and allies

The familiar fir trees, conifers and allies, also known as **gymnosperms**, presently dominate the high latitude forests of the northern hemisphere. During the Mesozoic this group was the dominant vegetation over most of the Earth and consequently has an excellent fossil record. The earliest true gymnosperms probably appeared in the Carboniferous, and some genera, such as *Araucaria* from the Jurassic, still exist and can be considered true living fossils.

Brachyphyllum is a multi-branched tree similar to the living Norfolk Island Pine and Monkey Puzzle Tree. The leaves are broad and scale-like, clinging close to the stem. This was probably a modification for tolerating arid conditions. *Brachyphyllum* and closely related forms are relatively common in southern England and Germany. Cosmopolitan. **Upper Jurassic to Cretaceous.**

Metasequoia

Brachyphylum

224

Frond and pinnules
of *Elatocladus*

Fir cone
from *Pinus*

Metasequoia was known from fossil remains before it was discovered still living in 1944 in China. The tree may reach a height of 30 m. The leaves are thin, flat, elongate blades, arranged in pairs along frond-like stems. Cosmopolitan. **Cretaceous** to **present day**.

Elatocladus is a fir tree closely related to the giant redwoods, but the leaves are difficult to distinguish from *Metasequoia* and the Yew tree *Taxus*. It has elongate branched fronds with many narrow, long pinnules. Scotland. **Palaeocene**.

Fir cones. Most gymnosperms produce relatively large seed-bearing organs commonly called cones. As they are produced in large numbers, and often composed of relatively hard tissues, they occur frequently as fossils. The one illustrated here is from the pine tree *Pinus* (see p. 226).

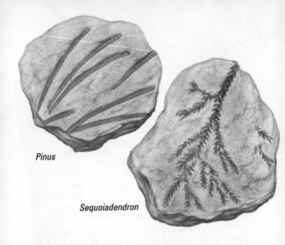

Pinus

Sequoiadendron

Pinus is the familiar pine tree which is so common over most of Europe and known to most people by the familiar cones and the needle-like leaves. Both leaves and cones occur frequently as fossils in the Tertiary of Europe. Cosmopolitan. Cretaceous to present day.

Sequoiadendron is the famous giant redwood tree of North America. Although now restricted as a wild tree to western USA, it formerly had a world-wide distribution. It has delicate, small elongate pinnules, pressed close to the stem. Cosmopolitan. Jurassic to present day.

Fossil forest with tree roots in place

Fossil forests

Occasionally entire forests become inundated by sediment when rivers are in flood, and the logs and tree stumps become preserved where they grew or fell. Spectacular examples of fossil forests occur in Arizona, USA where huge tree trunks rafted down a flooded river system and were buried in mud. They were later silicified, and even details of the internal cell structure are preserved. Fossil forests are also known from the Carboniferous of Scotland and the Jurassic of southern England.

Fossil forest of drifted logs

Ginkgo is an example of a living fossil. Leaves of *Ginkgo*, or Maidenhair tree, are known from the Triassic to the present, although they were more diverse in the Mesozoic than they are now. The *Ginkgo* tree reaches a height of up to 11 m, and has highly characteristic fan-shaped leaves with a radiating venation. The leaf may be divided into lobes. Common in the non-marine Jurassic of England, and the Palaeocene of the Isle of Mull, Scotland. Today, *Ginkgo* is native to China and is a very common ornamental tree in European parks and gardens. **Triassic** to **present day.**

Ginkgo

Flowering plants

This group, the **angiosperms**, is characterized by producing flowers. The sexes may be separate or on the same plant. Although highly variable in morphology, the angiosperms can be divided into two groups, the **monocotyledons** (monocots) which on germinating have a single leaf with parallel veins, and **dicotyledons** (dicots) which have two seed leaves, or **cotyledons**.

Typically dicots have broad leaves (although there are many exceptions) and monocots generally have narrow strap-like leaves. Angiosperms are found in a wide range of environments from the Arctic circle to the tropics. Many can withstand long periods of drought, some are parasitic and a few are carnivorous. Many forms have evolved elaborate relationships with animals, especially for purposes of fertilization, and they so far have colonized just about every environment on Earth except Antarctica. Many are deciduous and have been able even to colonize the highest latitudes where it is dark for almost six months of the year. Angiosperms are exceptionally common fossils in latest Mesozoic and Cenozoic non-marine sediments. The earliest undoubted occurrences of angiosperms are from the Lower Cretaceous.

Fossil angiosperms are common throughout Europe, but they are sometimes a little difficult to collect as many of the localities that yield their leaves are in poorly consolidated or loose sediments. Beautifully preserved leaves occur in the tertiary lignite deposits of Germany, where in some cases the preservation is so good that details of cell structure can be observed under a microscope.

Araliopsoides is a tree with large, tri-lobed leaves with continuous margin. This is a Cretaceous genus, but related forms survive to the present day.

Daphnogene or laurel has slender leaves terminating in a point. The margins are continuous. The laurel group is distributed world-wide. Palaeocene to present day.

Liquidamber is a large tree with five-pointed leaves with the two points closest to the stem being much smaller than the other three. The central point is usually the largest. Common over most of Europe. Oligocene to present day.

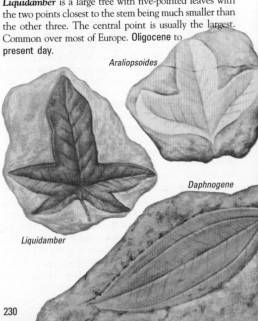

Araliopsoides

Daphnogene

Liquidamber

Single frond of
Sabalites x 0.1

Palms

Sabalites, a spectacular palm, is a common fossil in the
Eocene Green River Formation of Wyoming, USA,
where entire fronds occur. Related palms also occur in
European Tertiary sediments, but rarely are they so complete. Fruits of palms are commonly found in the Eocene
clays of the Isle of Sheppey, Kent, where they are preserved in iron pyrite. They can easily be picked up on the
beach at low tide.

Quercus

Populus

Carpinus

Many of the trees that are a familiar part of our modern deciduous forests are also known as fossils from the Tertiary. They are easy to identify because of their characteristic shapes and patterns of venation. The fossil remains of the modern flora are extremely useful, as they are of great value in charting changes in global climate over the last 50 million years. In this respect, the fossil pollen of these plants is just as important as the fossil leaves. The leaves illustrated here are frequently found in modern deposits of tufa, a form of calcium carbonate that forms at springs in limestone country. There are many places where these fossils can be found.

Populus, or the poplar trees, have broad to tapering leaves, often with slightly toothed margin. Found all over Europe. **Eocene** to **present day**.

Quercus or the oak trees have striking leaves, with lobed margins and well defined venation. Common over all of Europe. **Eocene** to **present day**.

Carpinus is the genus which includes the familiar birch trees. The leaves are moderately elongate, tapering, and have a finely serrated margin. Common over most of Europe. **Latest Cretaceous** to **present day**.

TRACE FOSSILS

Trace Fossils are more common than body fossils in some sedimentary rocks, and are very diverse in both mode of production and morphology. The following is just a selection of some of the more common forms.

Borings are made in hard substrates such as rock and wood. Many organisms produce borings: from microscopic bacteria to large echinoids and molluscs. *Lithophaga* is a bivalve mollusc that bores into rocks. Frequently the shell of the bivalve remains inside the boring. In cross-section the boring is flask shaped, with a narrow entrance. Common in **Mesozoic** and **Cenozoic** limestones throughout Europe.

Small borings that are slightly elongate and produced by a type of barnacle are called **Zapfella**. They are common on oyster shells in the Jurassic of England, and may be so numerous as to severely weaken the shell. Today *Zapfella* are common on boulders of chalk on modern beaches in front of the chalk cliffs of the English Channel and North Sea. **Jurassic** to **present day.**

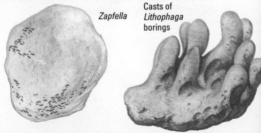

Zapfella

Casts of
Lithophaga
borings

Burrows are made in soft sediment by many organisms either to hide from predators or in search of food.

Thalassinoides is a horizontal branching burrow system with a diameter of 1-2 cm. The burrow is thicker where branches intersect. It is constructed by a type of shrimp and is very common in Mesozoic limestones over most of Europe. Shrimps that make these burrow systems are still alive today.

Diplocraterion is a U-shaped burrow system that often shows progressive deepening of the burrow as a series of growth increments called **spreite**. Most *Diplocraterion* burrows are constructed by annelids. Common as fossils; from the Mesozoic to present day.

Zoophycus is a mining system produced by an unknown organism while feeding on detritus in sediment. The organism swept through the sediment producing a fan-shaped feeding trace. As one level was exhausted it moved to greater depth.

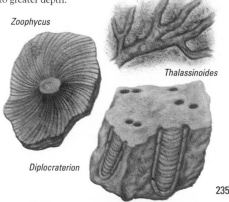

Zoophycus

Thalassinoides

Diplocraterion

Many organisms leave tracks and trails such as footprints or burrows during their life, and such traces can be common fossils. It is not often possible to match a track to the animal by any means other than circumstantial evidence, but occasionally an animal is found fossilized at the end of its track. Such is the case in a specimen of **Mesolimulus** from the **Jurassic** of Germany.

Chondrites is the name given to a system of fine branching burrows made by a possibly worm-like organism which fed on organic detritus within the sediment. The *Chondrites* animal, whatever it was, could tolerate low oxygen levels, but it is never preserved. **Cambrian** to **present day**.

Cruziana is the name given to long trails produced by an arthropod (possibly trilobites) in which there is a trough-like groove with a central ridge and rows of chevron-like markings. They were clearly made by a symmetrical animal with many limbs moving over the sediment. Common worldwide in the **Lower Palaeozoic**.

Dinosaur footprints

Tracks of vertebrate footprints can be very common in sediments deposited in inter-tidal mud flats and dry lake and river beds. Especially common are the highly distinctive footprints of dinosaurs and other large reptiles. The footprints of meat-eating dinosaurs are pointed prints made by sharp claws. Fossil footprints are known over most of Europe, from the Carboniferous to the present day, but dinosaur footprints are restricted to the Mesozoic. Good localities to see dinosaur and other reptile trackways are the coast at Scarborough, Yorkshire, and on the foreshore of the river Severn estuary in South Wales. They should be left in place.

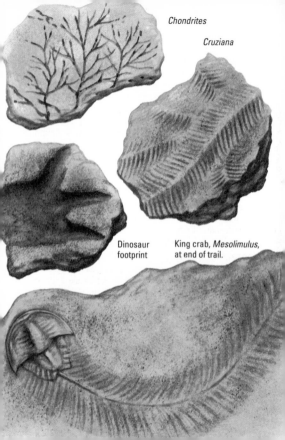

Chondrites

Cruziana

Dinosaur footprint

King crab, *Mesolimulus*, at end of trail.

SEDIMENTARY STRUCTURES

Sedimentary rocks may contain features produced by water or wind action at the time the sediment was deposited. These fabrics, called sedimentary structures, provide important clues for determining the environmental conditions prevailing at the time.

Ripple marks, produced by wind and water, can be used to determine the direction of ancient currents or trade winds.

Mudcracks are produced when fine grained sediments dry out in the sun, and are especially common in areas where shallow lakes dry up during hot summers.

Raindrop imprints are produced when exposed soft sediment is rained on.

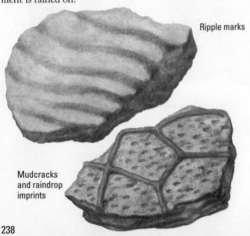

Ripple marks

Mudcracks
and raindrop
imprints

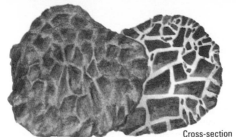

Cross-section

Septarian concretion

PSEUDOFOSSILS

Pseudofossils are objects found in rocks that look as though they might be organic remains, but in fact are not. Many of the processes that change sediment into rock can produce objects with strange shapes called **nodules** or **concretions**. These often resemble organic remains, the most common of which are nodules of chert or flint. Flint nodules often have stripes on them which make them look like segmented animals such as annelids or trilobites. Concretions composed of calcium carbonate often have star-shaped cracks inside which can easily be mistaken for plants or vertebrates.

Flint nodule from the chalk

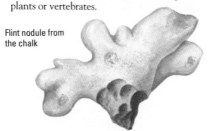

GLOSSARY OF TERMS

Abraded Worn and damaged, usually due to attrition by hard sediment particles.

Ammonitic Resembling an ammonite, or a feature of an ammonite, e.g. suture pattern.

Anastomosing Multibranching, apparently randomly.

Aperture The opening of a shell from which the organism protrudes.

Arcuate Curved in an arch. Often used when referring to the shape of a shell, or to curved ribs on the surface of a shell.

Bedding planes Surfaces in sedimentary rocks that represent minor disruptions or changes in style of sedimentation. Sedimentary rocks usually split easily along bedding planes to reveal fossils.

Bifurcate Splitting into two.

Bioimmuration The overgrowth of one organism by another. Usually results in the death of the bioimmured organism.

Calcitic Composed of calcite.

Carapace The external shell of an arthropod, usually enclosing most of the animal. Also used to refer to the 'shells' of turtles.

Cartilaginous Composed of cartilage, a tough, non-mineralized material from which the skeletons of sharks are composed.

Chambered Divided into numerous chambers, as in the shells of ammonites and nautiloids.

Cirri Small appendages on the stems of crinoids.

Colonial Group of organisms living together and usually connected by soft tissues. May all be genetically identical, e.g. colonial coral.

Concretion A mass of stone, usually rounded, which grew by accretion during diagenesis, often around a fossil. May be composed of a variety of minerals, but concretions of calcium carbonate are especially abundant in clays. They are a good source of well preserved 3-D fossils (see also nodule).

Cosmopolitan Very widespread, often of global distribution.

Crenulated A wavy margin, may become serrated.

Crenulations Margin with indentations.

Detritus Usually organic, refers to debris that can be eaten by some omnivores.

Diagenesis Chemical and biochemical process occurring within sediment that may result in converting the sediment into rock, and change organic remains into fossils.

Disarticulated A skeleton in which the various components that were once attached, are now separated. This can be due to scavenging, current activity, or simply gravity collapse during decomposition.

Discoidal Shaped like a disc.

Distal Some distance away from source. For example, fine sediment is distal if it is deposited along way from the area from where it was eroded. Alternatively, parts of an organism can be considered proximal, near to the body, or distal, away from the body. Fingers are distal.

Dorsal On the upper surface, for example the dorsal fin of fish lies on the back.

Elongate Long relative to width.

Encrusting Organisms that live on the surface of other organisms or on hard parts of the sea floor are called encrusters; many bryozoans and oysters for example.

Era A long time period, usually of several tens or hundreds of millions of years and characterized by major geological and/or biological processes. Major extinctions may be used to define the end of an era.

Evolute In spiral shells evolute is used to refer to shells in which it is possible to see most of each of the earlier whorls (see also involute).

Evolution The process of morphological change observed in organisms through time due to presumed changes in the composition of genetic material.

Exoskeleton A skeleton which is on the outside of the body. This is the case with arthropods. External skeletons restrict growth, and must be shed periodically. Such parts of exoskeletons are very common as fossils.

Flanges Extensions, usually thin, beyond the main body.

Frond A leaf-like structure composed of a central stem with many lateral branches each with smaller leaves or pinnules. Typically found in ferns and palms.

Fossil Trace of ancient life found in the rock record.

Genal Refers to the cheek. Used to describe some spines on the head shields of trilobites that are extensions of the free cheek.

Helical Twisted in a spiral in which the coiling is both outwards and downwards. As in common garden snail *Helix*.

Heteromorph A term used to refer to ammonites which do not produce planispirally coiled shells.

Instars Growth stages of arthropods between moults.

Involute A term used to describe coiled shells in which the coiling overlaps much of the preceding coil. Some shells may overlap all of the preceding coils producing ball-like shells (see also evolute).

Keel A prominent ridge on an otherwise regular surface. Commonly found on the ventral surface of some ammonites. Keels may be simple or highly ornamented. They may be crenulated (see above).

Lappets Extensions of the shell at the margin of some ammonites. Believed to be sexually dimorphic structures found only on male ammonites.

Laterally compressed Flattened from the sides.

Living fossil A living animal or plant that is known to have a long fossil record showing little morphological change over time; or a living animal with primitive characteristics, despite not having a fossil record; or an animal or plant that was known from fossil remains before being discovered to be alive today, as in the case of the coelacanth.

Lobes Extensions of a structure which are usually rounded. Also refers to part of ammonite suture which projects towards origin.

Lunate Shaped like the crescent moon.

Mass extinction A time, usually short on a geological scale, when the number of extinctions far exceeds the number of new species evolving. A number of mass extinctions are known from the fossil record, notably at the end of the Permian and the end of the Cretaceous. These extinctions define the end of the Palaeozoic and Mesozoic eras.

Medially Towards or in the middle.

Morphology Refers to shape.

Neomorphism The conversion of one material to another without any disruption of the original microstructure. For example, aragonite will neomorphose to calcite over time with the retention of original shell structure.

Nodule A rounded mass of stone often found in clays which may have formed around a fossil (see concretion).

Organelles Structures within individual cells that perform a variety of important biochemical functions, e.g. the mitochondria.

Ornament Patterning seen on the surface of shells. This term is going out of use, as most structures observed on shells are not for ornamentation, but perform a specific function, e.g. ribs with spines on bivalves anchor the shell in soft sediment.

Orthoconic A straight cone.

Palaeontology The study of ancient life.

Phanerozoic The time period represented by sediments containing shelly fossils. Began approximately 540 million years ago; has not ended.

Photosynthetic Derives its energy from sunlight using a variety of complex chemical steps, whereby carbon dioxide is converted by plants into more complex molecules.

Phragmacone The chambered part of the shell of cephalopods.

Phyla A taxonomic rank that is based on basic body plans. No phylum of the phanerozoic is thought to have become extinct and all animal phyla alive today are thought to have originated in the Cambrian.

Planispiral Coiled in a single plane.

Planktonic Living in surface waters, drifting with the

currents. Some organisms may spend all their life as plankton, others may have only larval or adult stages in the plankton.

Polygonal With many sides, e.g. a hexagon.

Pseudopodia Extensions of cell material beyond the main body of the cell.

Processes Extensions beyond the main outline.

Proximally Close to the body or towards the body (see also distally).

Recurved Curved backwards.

Reticulated Pattern of irregular polygons. As in the colour pattern of a giraffe.

Saddles Refers to the part of an ammonite suture pattern that projects towards the aperture.

Septal Of a septum, the wall that separates chambers in cephalopod phragmacones.

Septate Divided into chambers by partitions which in cephalopods are called septa.

Silica An oxide of silicon SiO_2. Commonly occurs as the mineral quartz although other forms are known.

Silicified Converted from original material to silica by diagenetic processes (see diagenesis).

Siphonal Of the siphon; may refer to parts of the shell of gastropods and bivalves that are modified to protect large siphons used in feeding and respiration.

Siphuncle A tube in cephalopods that connects all of the chambers of the phragmacone.

Spicules Small mineralized needles often found in sponges and sea cucumbers. Can be calcite or silica in sponges but are calcite in sea cucumbers.

Spongin A proteinaceous material that sponges make their skeletons with. In some sponges it may be mineralized by calcite or silica.

Stereom An open, sponge-like texture found in the mineralized components of echinoderm skeletons.

Sub-spherical Almost spherical. Prefix may be used for variety of shapes, e.g. sub-triangular.

Substrate The surface on which an organism lives. Often refers simply to the sea floor.

Sulcus A depression, may be elongate and running between two keels or ridges.

Suture The line defined where a septum meets the body wall in cephalopods.

Test A complete shell.

Tetrapod An animal with four limbs. For example, frogs, birds and even snakes, despite their current lack of limbs.

Theca A cup-like structure that houses an organism. See graptolites.

Trifurcate Splitting into three.

Umbilicus A broad depression produced in coiled shells as the shell gets larger during coiling.

Unconsolidated Loose sediment.

Venation With a pattern of veins as in the wings of insects or the leaves of angiosperm plants.

Venter The lower surface.

Whorl A complete turn in a spiral shell.

Winnowing The exposure of coarse particles by the removal of fine particles by the action of wind or more commonly water.

INDEX OF GENERA

SUGGESTED FURTHER READING

Collins Photoguide to Fossils, H Mayr (HarperCollins)

Invertebrate palaeontology and evolution, E N K Clarkson (Allen & Unwin)

Vertebrate palaeontology, M J Benton (Unwin Hyman)

British Palaeozoic Fossils
British Mesozoic Fossils
British Caenozoic Fossils (Natural History Museum)

Field Guides to Fossils series (Palaeontological Association):
Fossil plants of the London Clay
Fossils of the Chalk
Zechstein reef fossils and their palaeoecology
Fossils of the Oxford Clay
Fossils of the Santana and Crato Formations, Brazil

GEOLOGICAL TIME CHART

The chart on pages 254-255 lists the geological eras from the beginning of the Earth to the present day. The eras are divided into systems and times, in millions of years, with dates given for the beginnings and ends of each of the systems within the eras.

Ranges for a variety of animal and plant groups are given adjacent to the time column. Within the text some systems are further divided by reference to older parts of a system, referred to as being Lower, or younger portions of the system, referred to as being Upper, e.g. Upper Jurassic or Lower Cretaceous. Middle is also used for some systems of long duration. When fossil ranges have not been determined accurately, some stratigraphic ranges are preceded by a question mark, e.g. ?Upper Jurassic. This may mean that a fossil of Upper Jurassic age has been tentatively identified as a given species, but perhaps remains to be confirmed, or that the exact date of a suite of rocks containing a given fossil remains to be established more accurately.

The dates given have been determined by radiometric analysis and are accurate generally to within less than one million years. The time for the base of the Cambrian is given as 570 million years and also as 540 million years ago. There is still some debate as to the exact age or the base of the Cambrian, but most authors prefer a date of 540 million years.

Era	System	Years ago (millions)
Quaternary	Holocene	Present–0.01
	Pleistocene	0.01–2.5
Cenozoic	Pliocene	2.5–5
	Miocene	5–20
	Oligocene	20–38
	Eocene	38–54
	Palaeocene	54–65
Mesozoic	Cretaceous	65–144
	Jurassic	144–208
	Triassic	208–245
Palaeozoic	Permian	245–286
	Carboniferous	286–360
	Devonian	360–408
	Silurian	408–438
	Ordovician	438–505
	Cambrian	505–570 (540)
Precambrian	Proterozoic	570–2500
	Archaean	2500–3500
	Hadean	3500–5000?

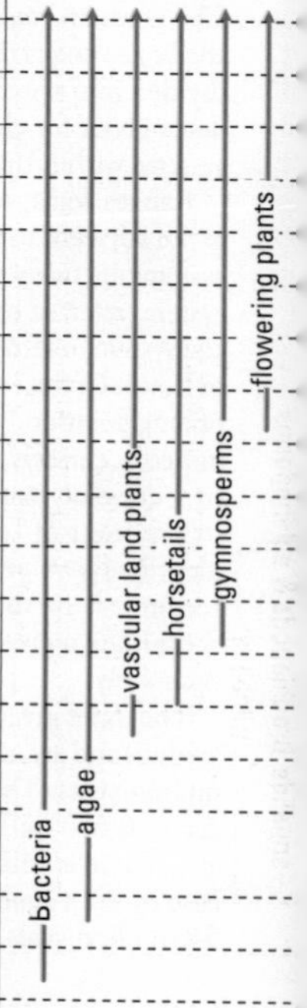

bacteria
algae
vascular land plants
horsetails
gymnosperms
flowering plants

annelids, brachiopods & echinoderms
trilobites
nautiloid cephalopods
ammonoids
graptolites
conodonts, lampreys & agnathans
sharks
bony fish
amphibians
reptiles
crocodiles
turtles
plesiosaurs & ichthyosaurs
dinosaurs
birds
pterosaurs
mammals
humans

COLLINS GEM